Complete Scales and Arpeggios for piano

Faber Music Bloomsbury House 74–77 Great Russell Street London WC1B 3DA
in association with Trinity College London

Contents

Pentatonic and blues scales by Simon Purcell

First published in 2005 by Faber Music Ltd
in association with Trinity College London
Bloomsbury House
74–77 Great Russell Street
London WC1B 3DA
Cover design by Sarah Theodosiou
Page layout design by Sue Clarke
Music processed by Stave Origination
Printed in England by Caligraving Ltd

ISBN10: 0-571-52192-4
EAN13: 978-0-571-52192-0

To buy Faber Music or Trinity publications or to find out about the full range of titles available
please contact your local music retailer or Faber Music sales enquiries:

Faber Music Ltd, Burnt Mill, Elizabeth Way, Harlow CM20 2HX
Tel: +44 (0)1279 82 89 82 Fax: +44 (0)1279 82 89 83
sales@fabermusic.com fabermusicstore.com trinitycollege.com

Foreword

Whether you view your work on scales and arpeggios as a necessary evil or a wonderful opportunity to explore the intricacies of piano technique, you will need a reliable and authoritative resource book. *Complete Scales and Arpeggios for Piano* distills the best of current practice into a publication which is easy to read and is laid out in a clear and logical way. The contents have been thoroughly researched and the whole has been brought together under the expert guidance of John York.

In addition to the scales and arpeggios themselves, John York has provided comprehensive and helpful notes to help pupils get the best out of their scale practice. There is important advice which will ensure that the effects of scale and arpeggio practice are wholly positive, avoiding the aches, pains or more serious injuries that can befall the young pianist!

One final plea to piano students: in order for scale and arpeggio practice to be useful and to protect your own health and safety, it must be a consistent part of your practice – not something you cram in just before the exam. With this book you have the opportunity to discover just what a short-cut to musical and technical progress your work on scales and arpeggios can be. We hope you enjoy working with it.

C major

The relative minor of C major is A minor.

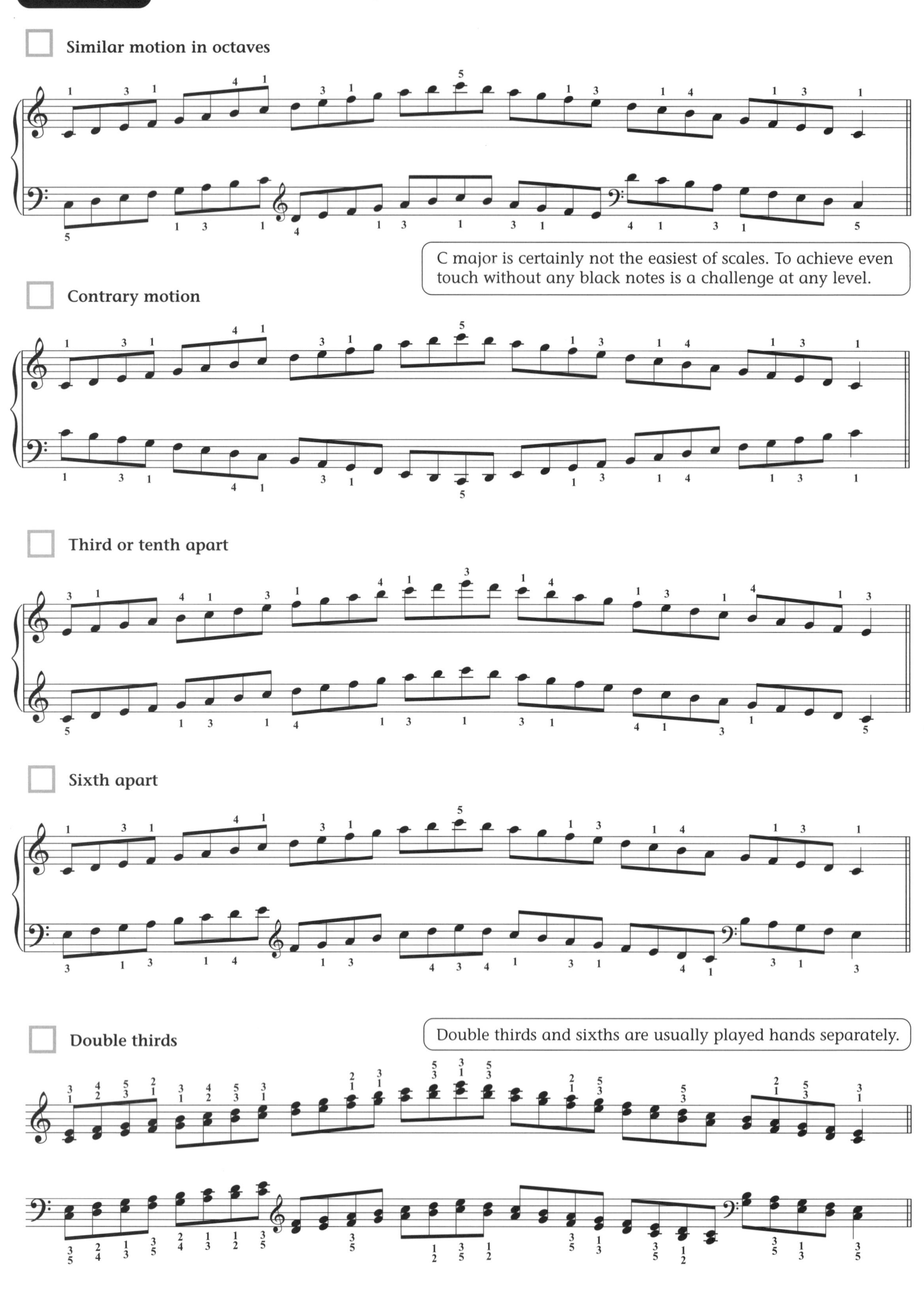

C major arpeggio

☐ **Root position**

☐ **First inversion**

☐ **Second inversion**

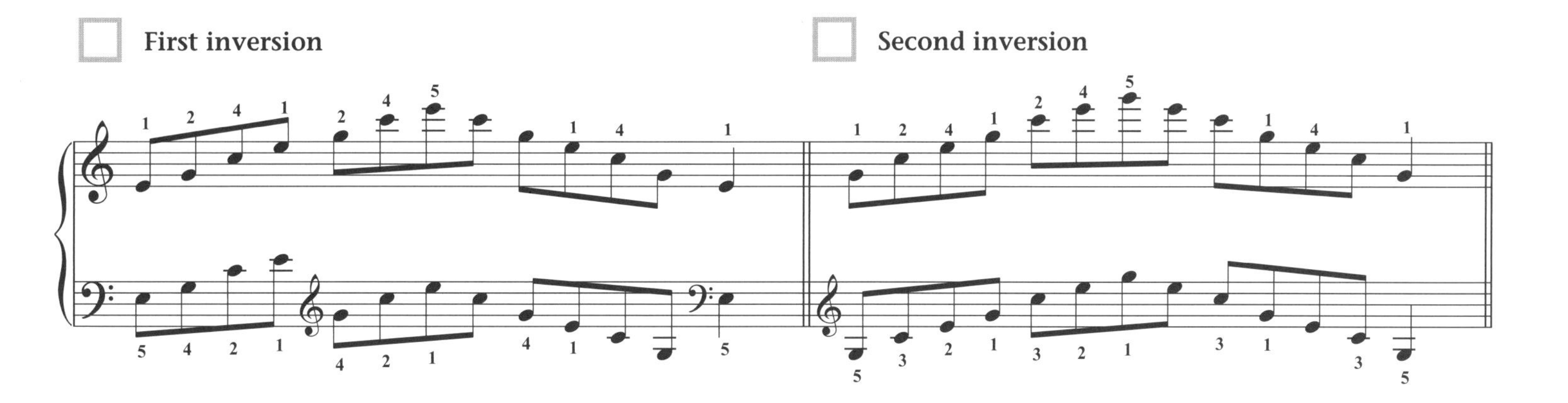

Dominant and diminished sevenths

☐ **Dominant seventh in C**

☐ **Diminished seventh on C**

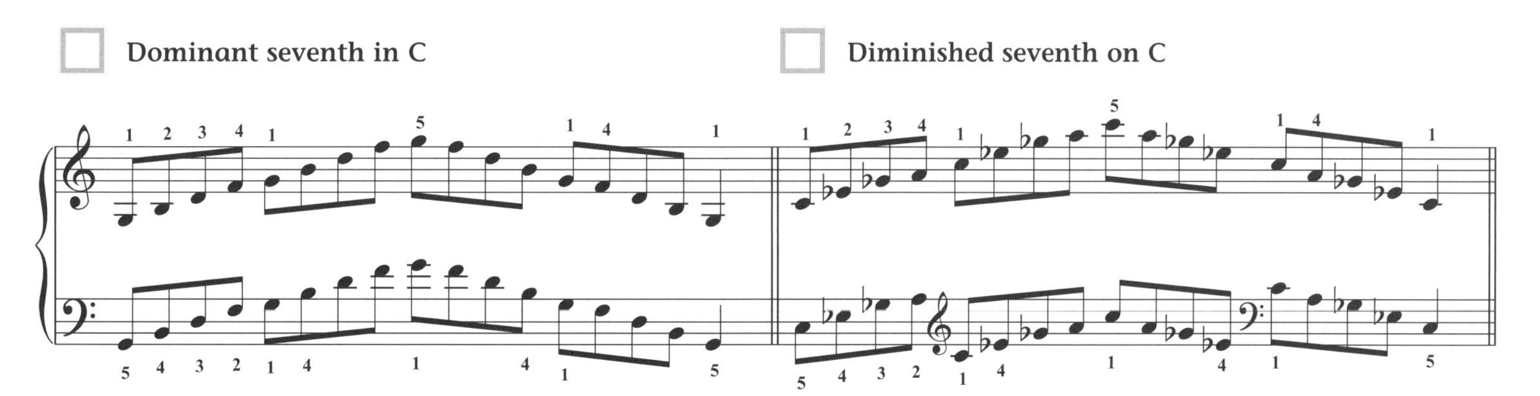

Hints and tips

- Scales in double thirds can be fingered in many ways; the system adopted here is the 'two group' fingering. Each octave is divided into a 3-note and 4-note group, the longer group using the gliding thumb.
- As well as practising using different variations of touch, tone, rhythm and range, you could try playing scales and arpeggios in keys related to C major: the relative minor (A minor), the dominant (G major), the subdominant (F major) and the tonic minor (C minor).
- Using the 3rd finger where 4th is stipulated in arpeggios is accepted by some pianists, but it is better to train the weaker 4th finger from the earliest lessons to encourage proper, systematic hand shape development.

C minor

The relative major of C minor is E♭ major.
Watch out for the raised seventh in C minor: B♮.

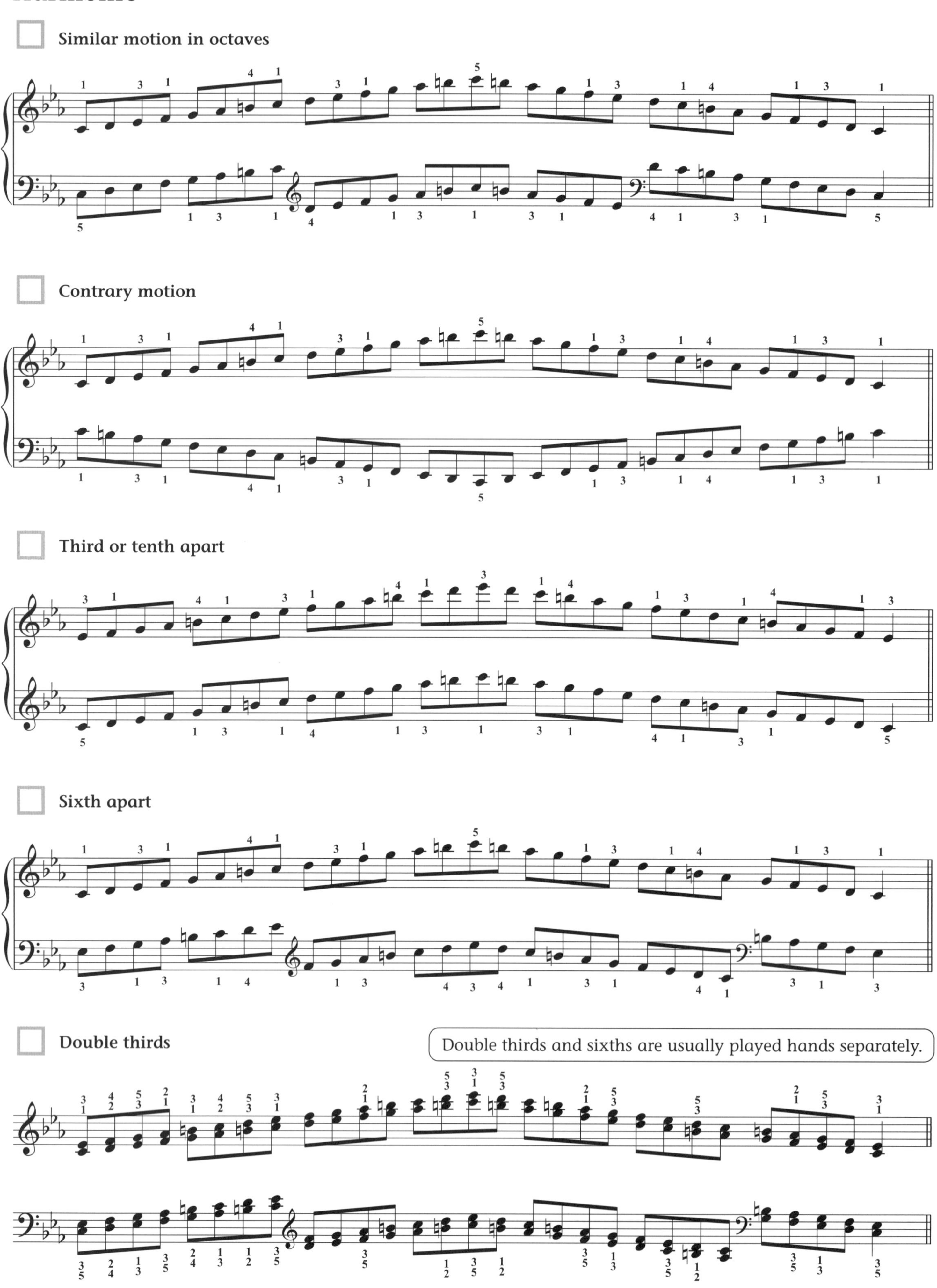

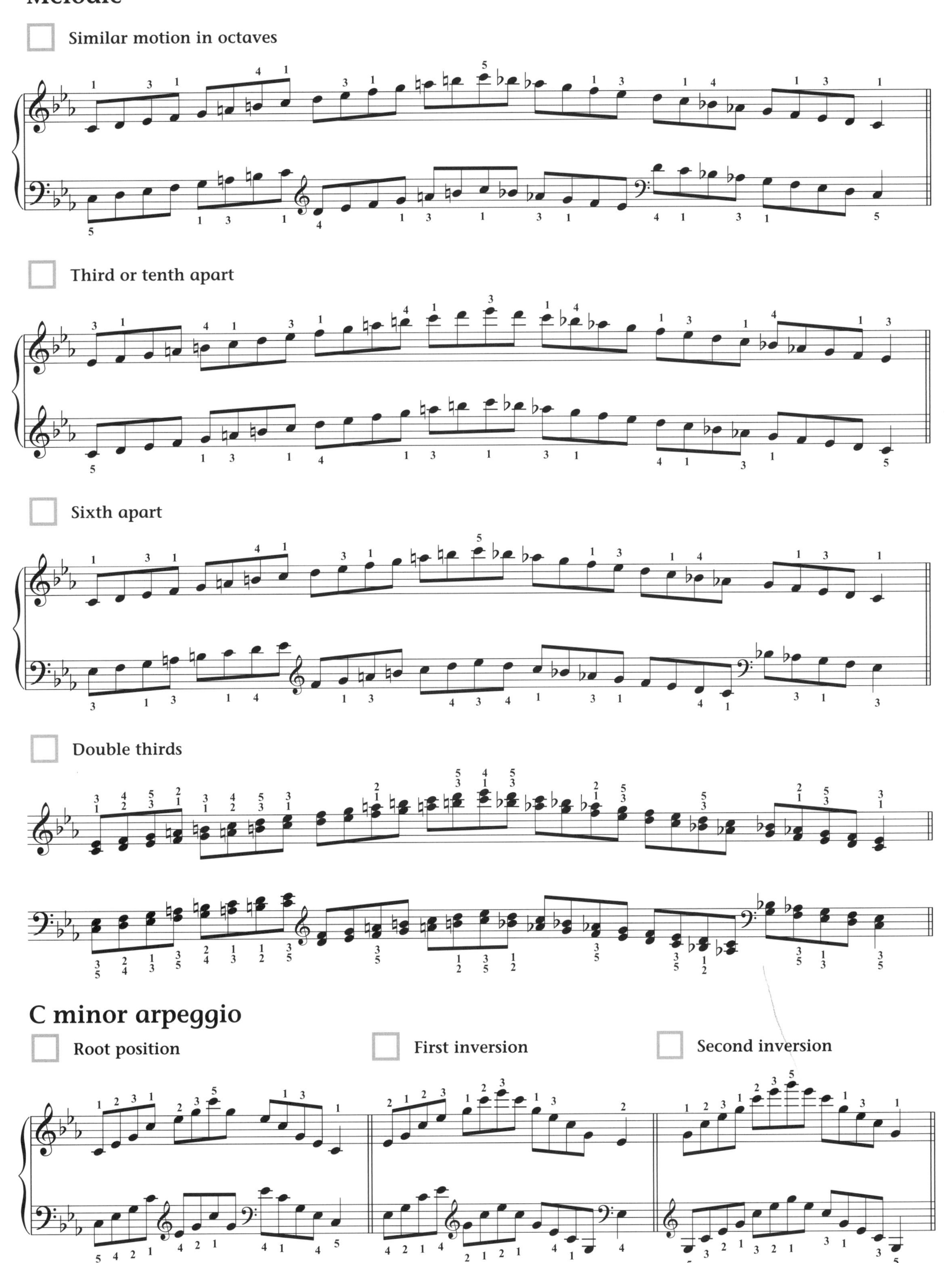
Melodic
Similar motion in octaves
Third or tenth apart
Sixth apart
Double thirds
C minor arpeggio
Root position
First inversion
Second inversion

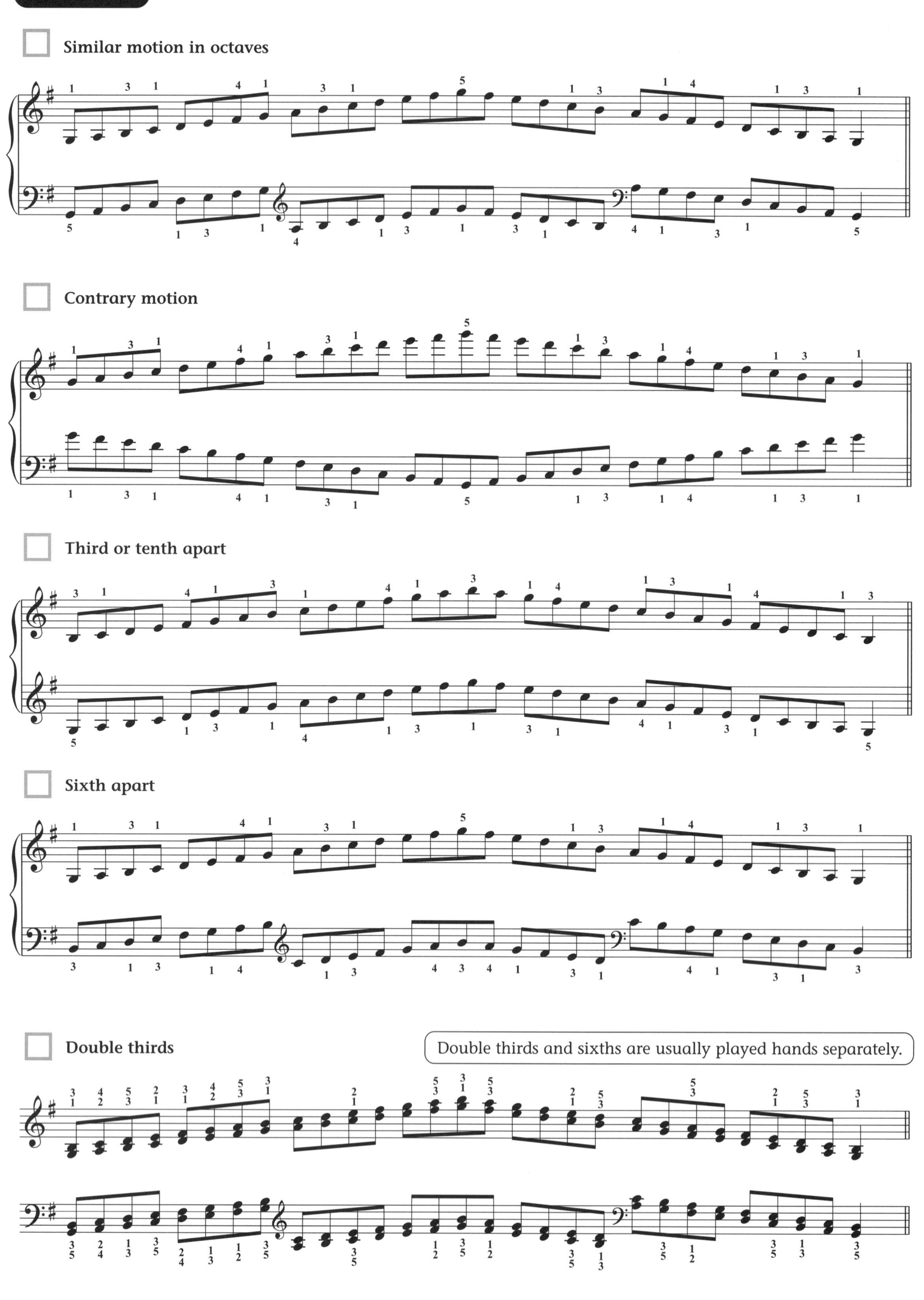
G major
The relative minor of G major is E minor.
Similar motion in octaves
Contrary motion
Third or tenth apart
Sixth apart
Double thirds
Double thirds and sixths are usually played hands separately.

G major arpeggio

☐ Root position

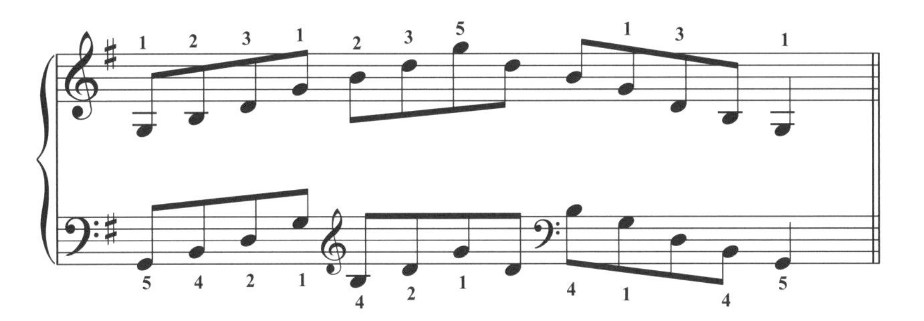

☐ First inversion

☐ Second inversion

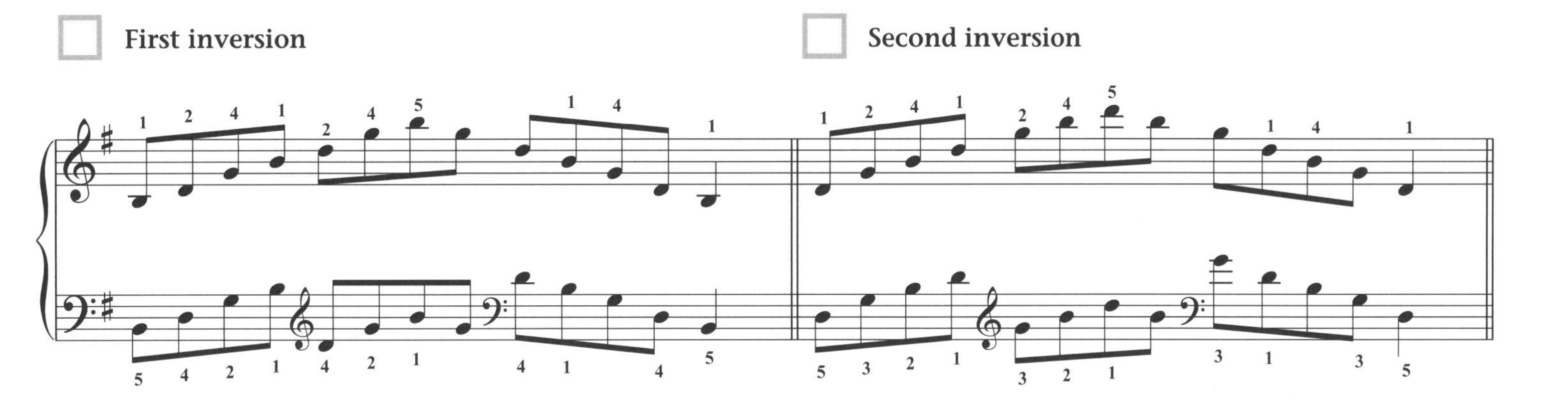

Dominant and diminished sevenths

☐ Dominant seventh in G

☐ Diminished seventh on G

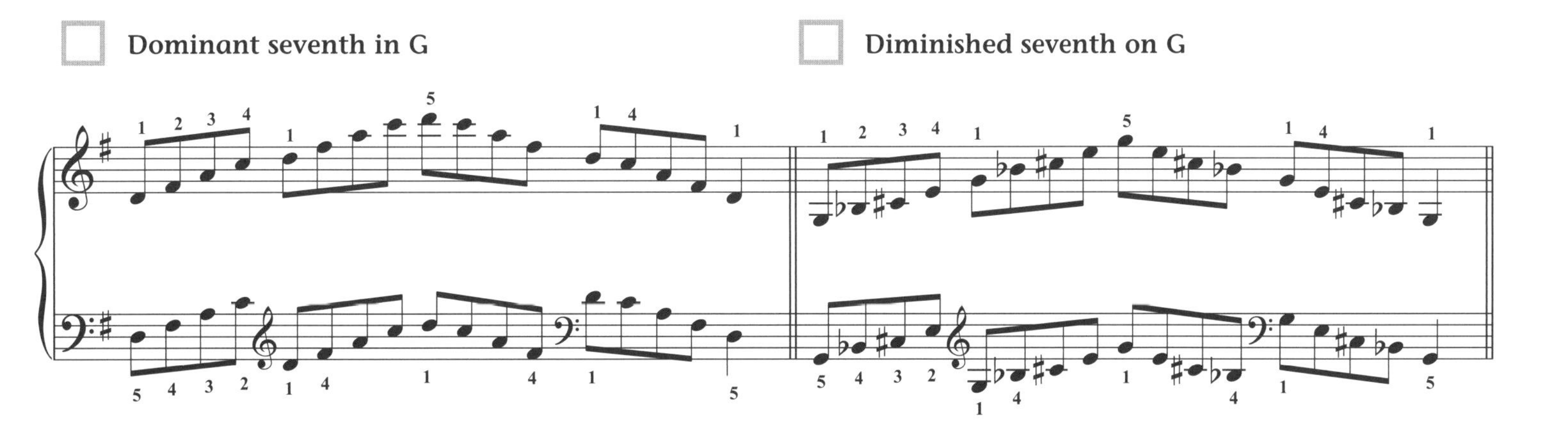

Hints and tips

- Scales in double thirds can be fingered in many ways; the system adopted here is the 'two group' fingering. Each octave is divided into a 3-note and 4-note group, the longer group using the gliding thumb.
- As well as practising using different variations of touch, tone, rhythm and range, you could try playing scales and arpeggios in keys related to G major: the relative minor (E minor), the dominant (D major), the subdominant (C major) and the tonic minor (G minor).
- Using the 3rd finger where 4th is stipulated in arpeggios is accepted by some pianists, but it is better to train the weaker 4th finger from the earliest lessons to encourage proper, systematic hand shape development.

G minor

The relative major of G minor is B♭ major.
Watch out for the raised seventh in G minor: F♯.

Harmonic

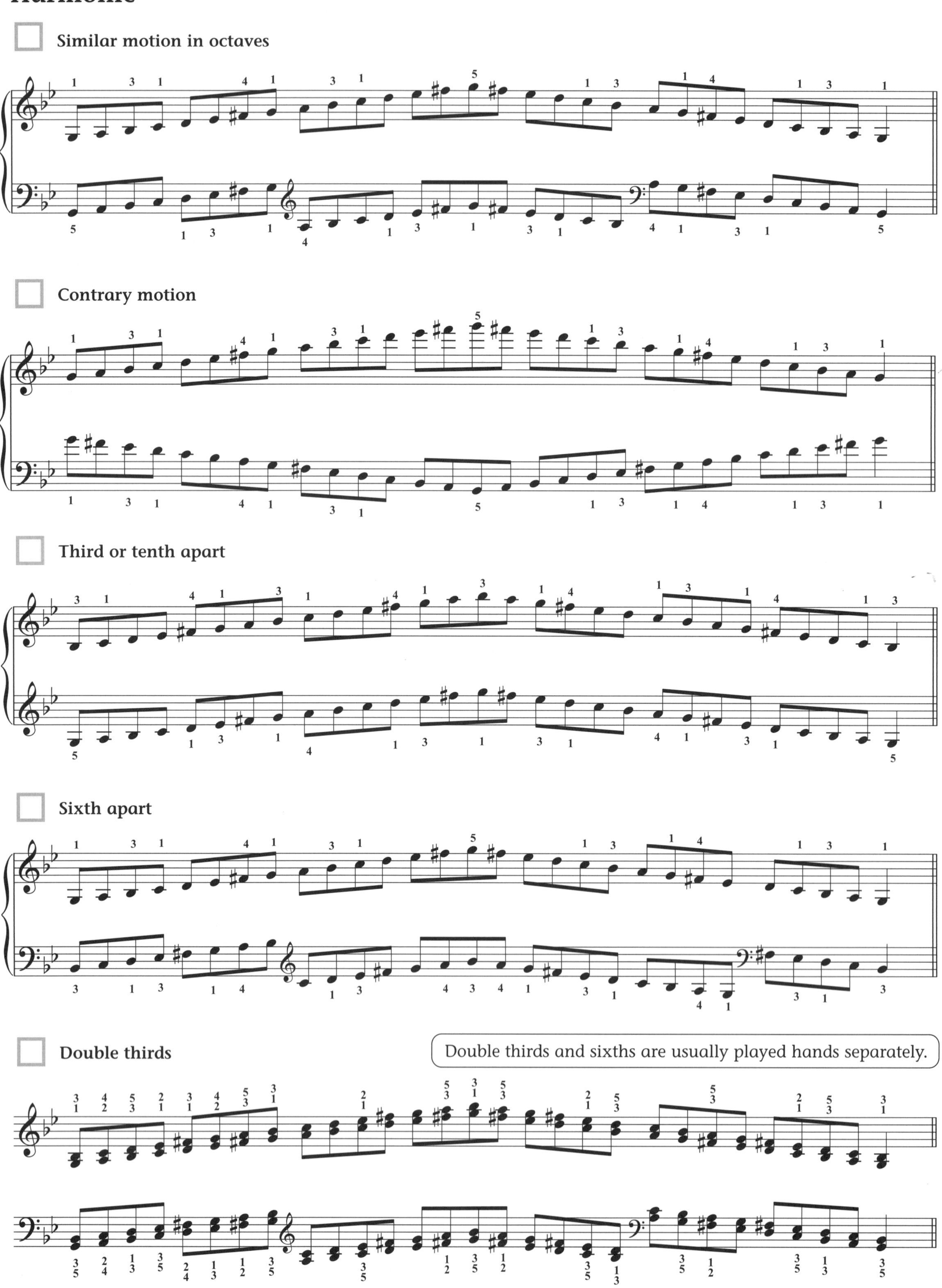

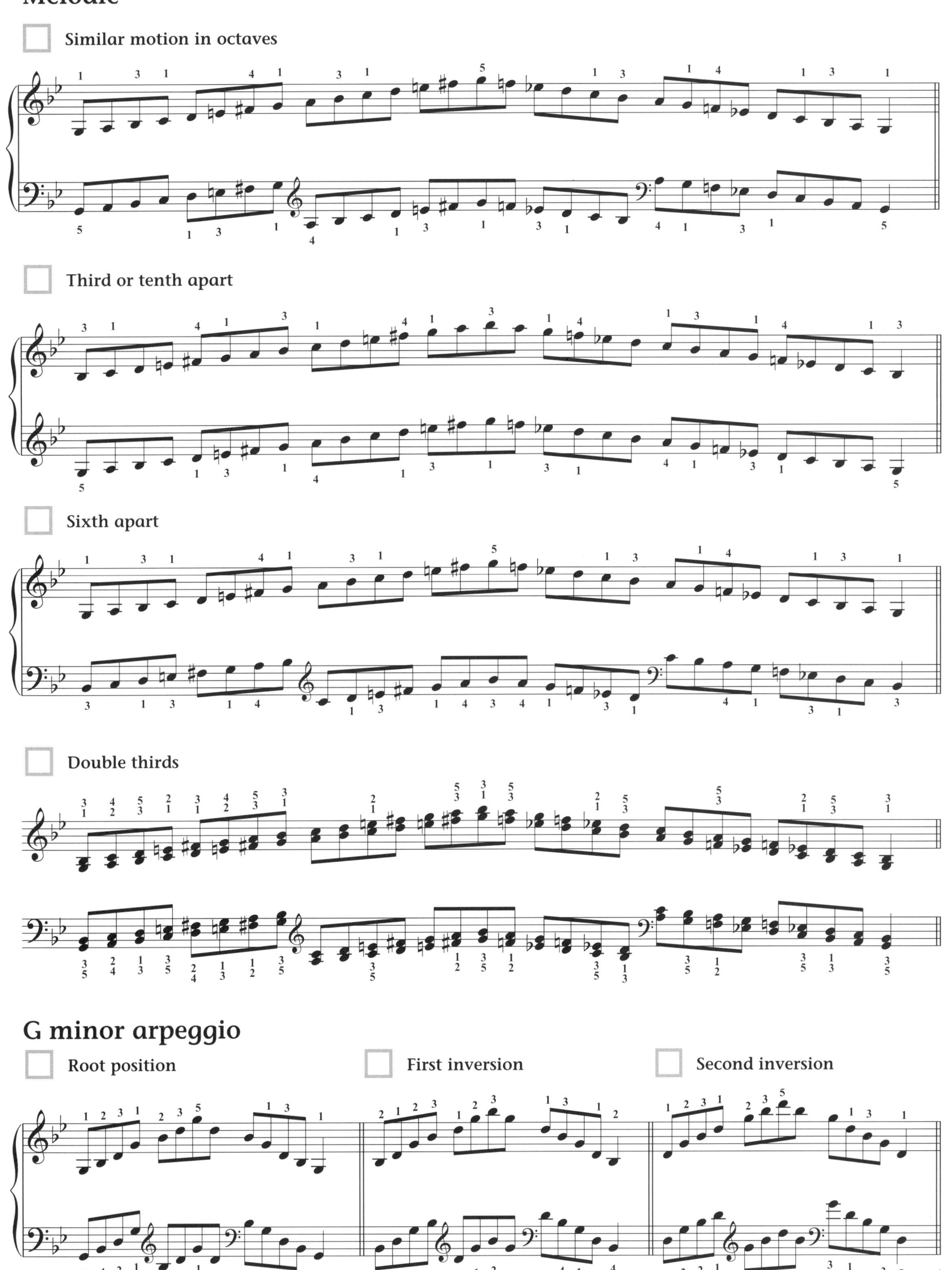
Melodic
Similar motion in octaves
Third or tenth apart
Sixth apart
Double thirds
G minor arpeggio
Root position
First inversion
Second inversion

D major

The relative minor of D major is B minor.

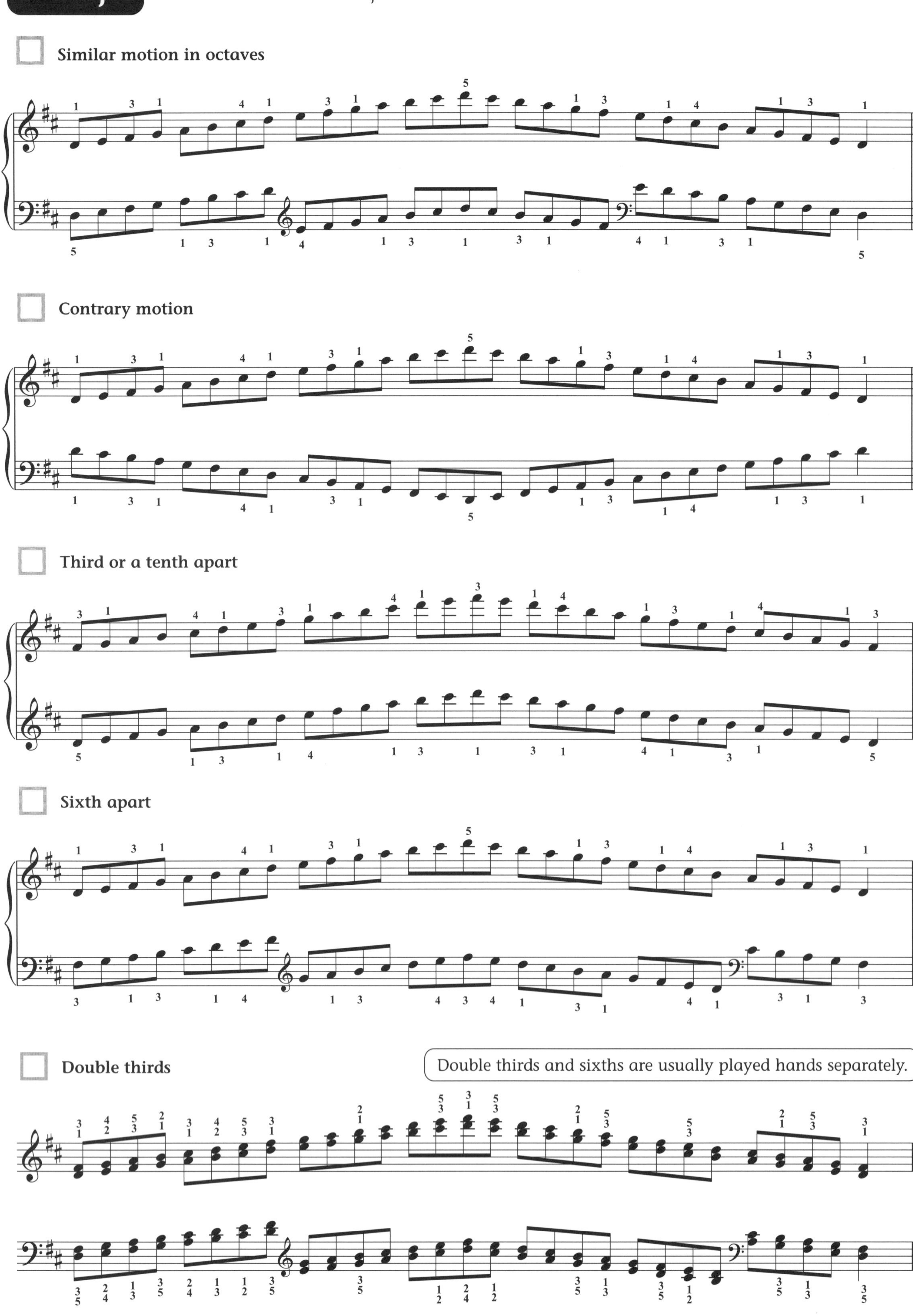

D major arpeggio

☐ Root position

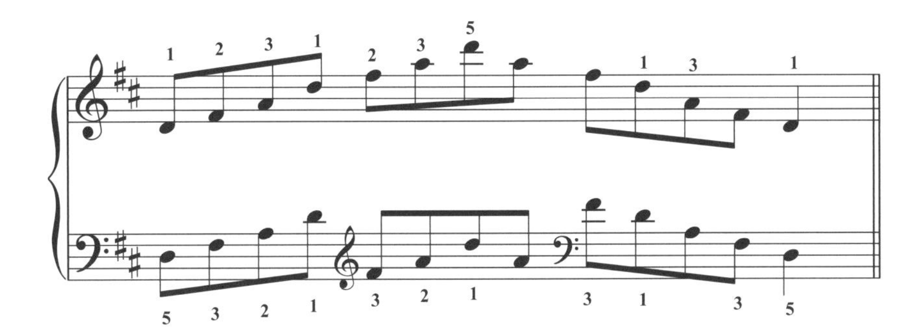

☐ First inversion

☐ Second inversion

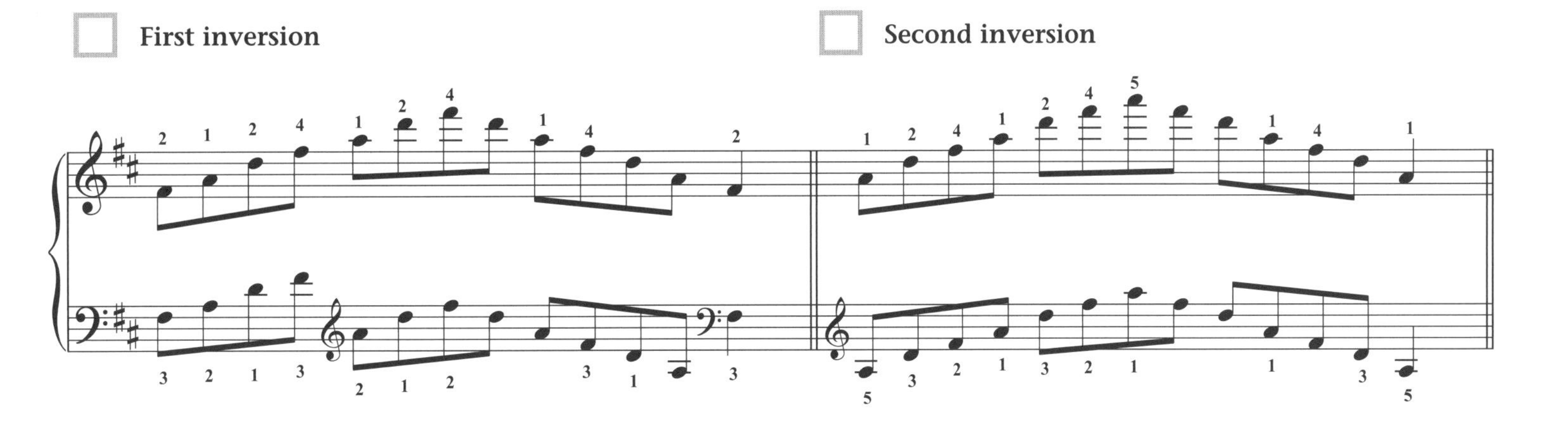

Dominant and diminished sevenths

☐ Dominant seventh in D

☐ Diminished seventh on D

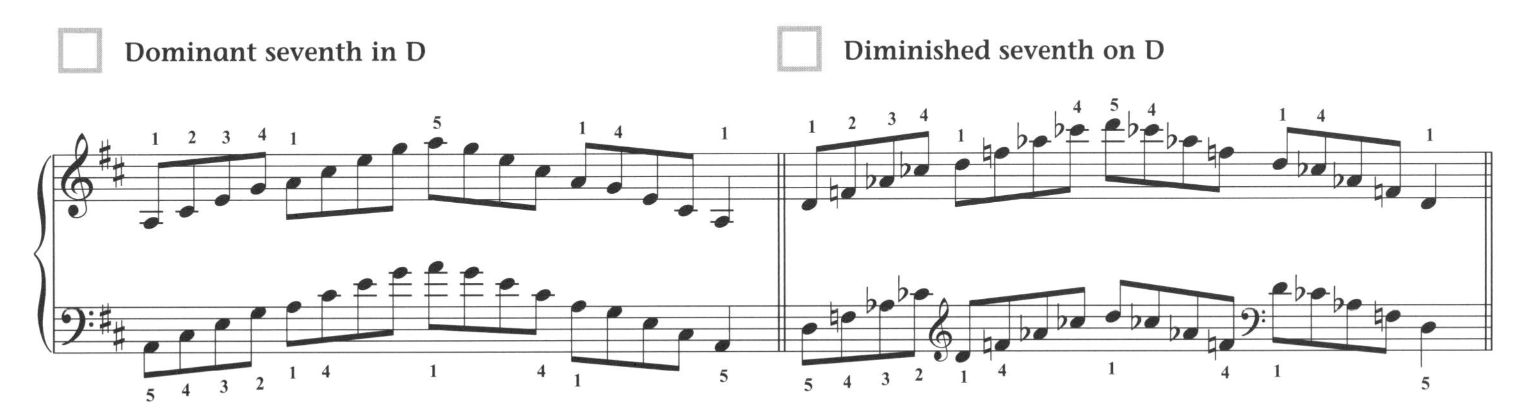

Hints and tips

- Scales in double thirds can be fingered in many ways; the system adopted here is the 'two group' fingering. Each octave is divided into a 3-note and 4-note group, the longer group using the gliding thumb.
- As well as practising using different variations of touch, tone, rhythm and range, you could try playing scales and arpeggios in keys related to D major: the relative minor (B minor), the dominant (A major), the subdominant (G major) and the tonic minor (D minor).
- Using the 3rd finger where 4th is stipulated in arpeggios is accepted by some pianists, but it is better to train the weaker 4th finger from the earliest lessons to encourage proper, systematic hand shape development.

D minor

The relative major of D minor is F major.
Watch out for the raised seventh in D minor: C♯.

Harmonic

Similar motion in octaves

Contrary motion

Third or tenth apart

Sixth apart

Double thirds

Double thirds and sixths are usually played hands separately.

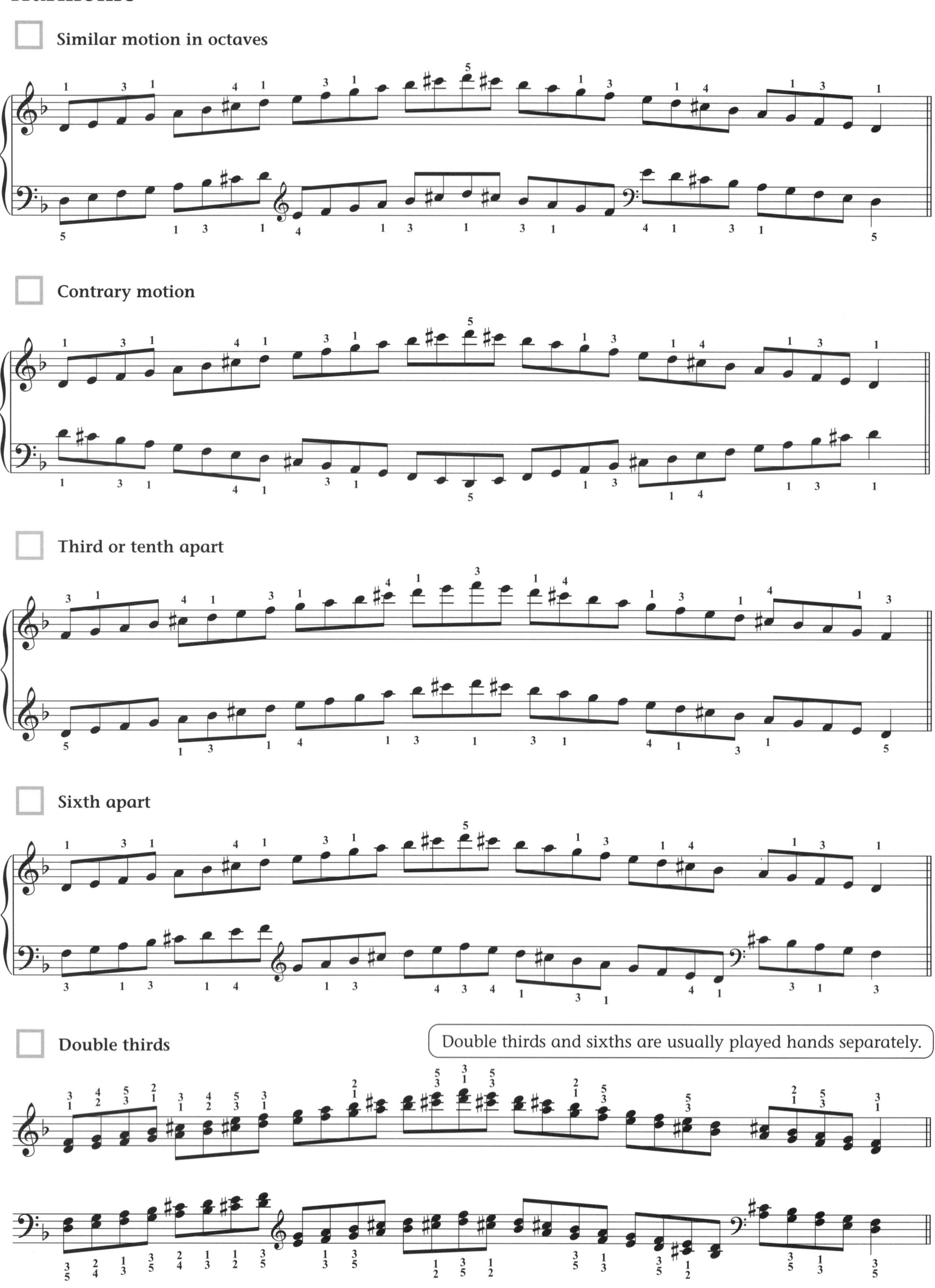

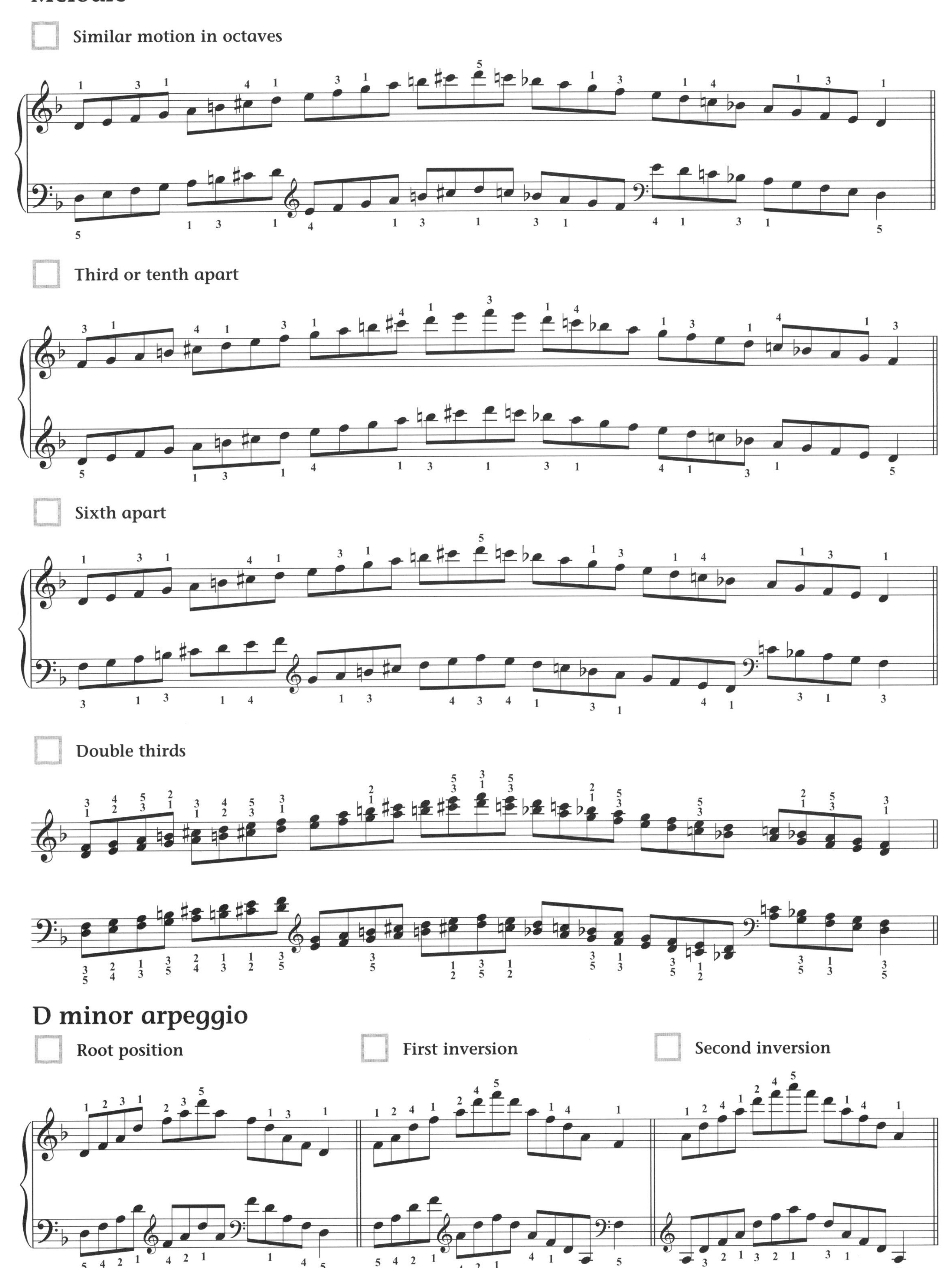
Melodic
Similar motion in octaves
Third or tenth apart
Sixth apart
Double thirds
D minor arpeggio
Root position
First inversion
Second inversion

A major

The relative minor of A major is F♯ minor.

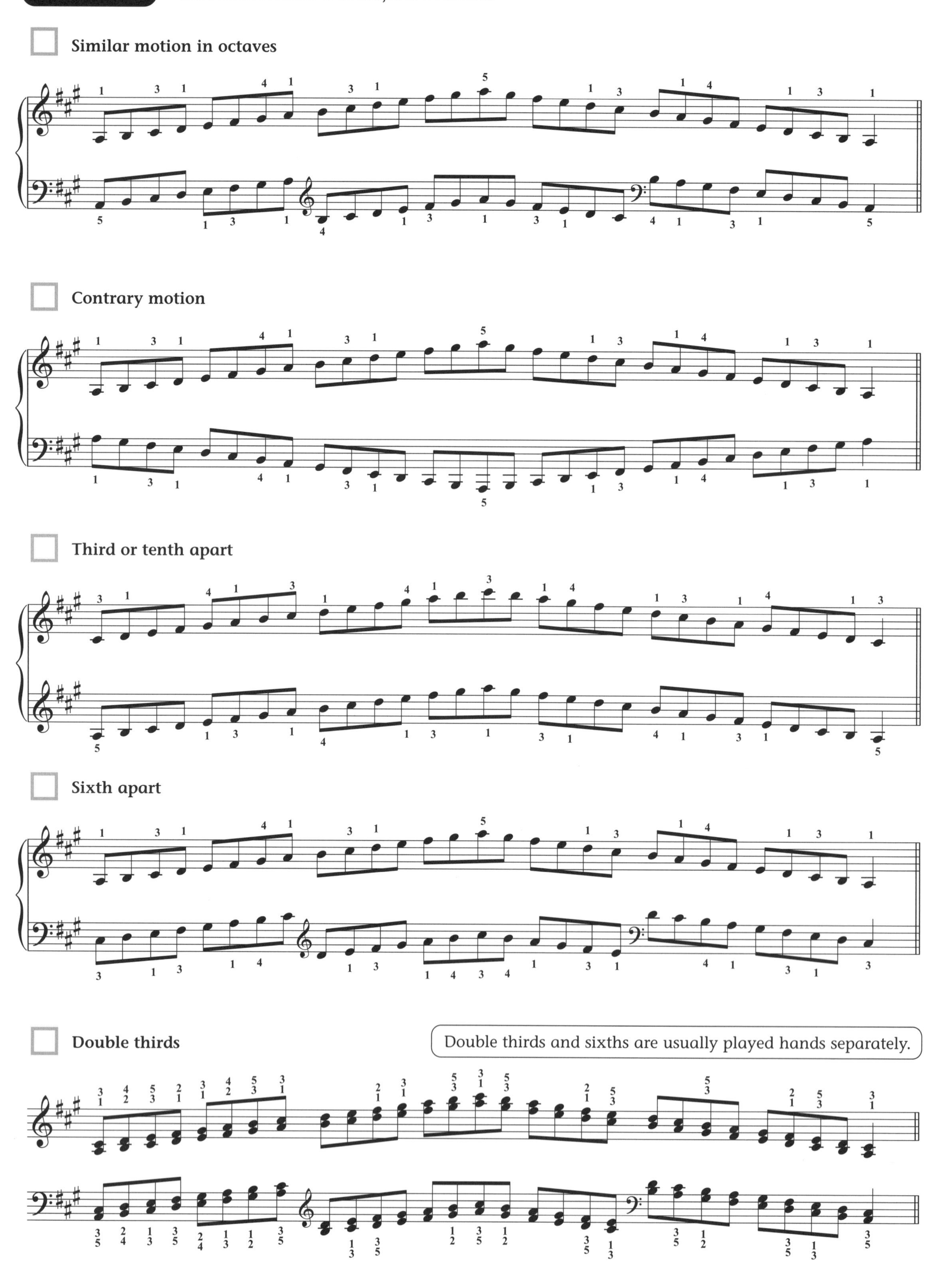

A major arpeggio

☐ Root position

☐ First inversion

☐ Second inversion

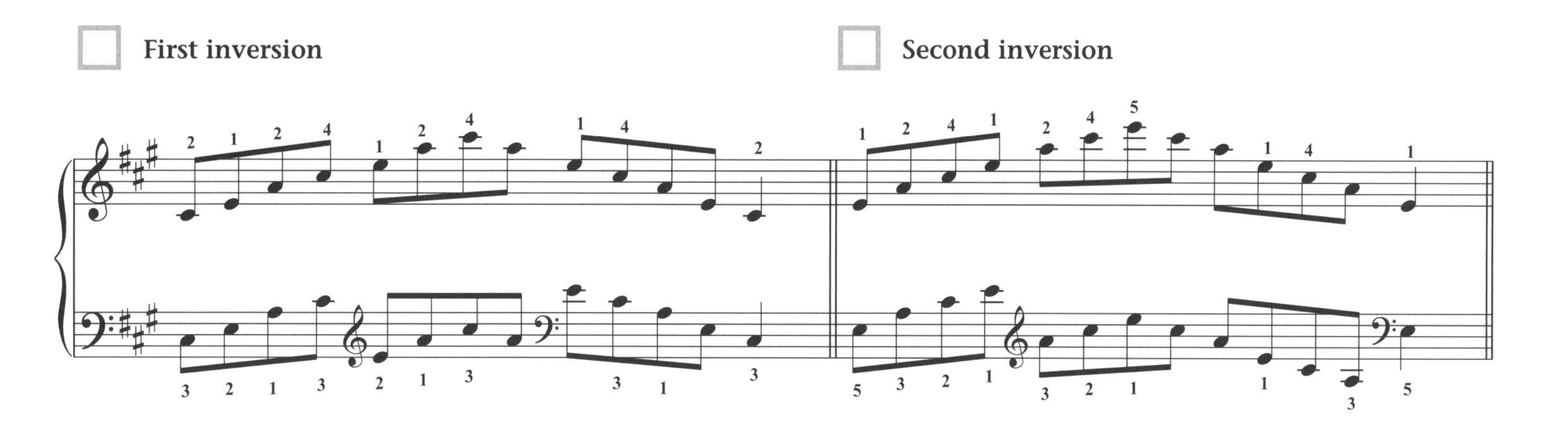

Dominant and diminished sevenths

☐ Dominant seventh in A

☐ Diminished seventh on A

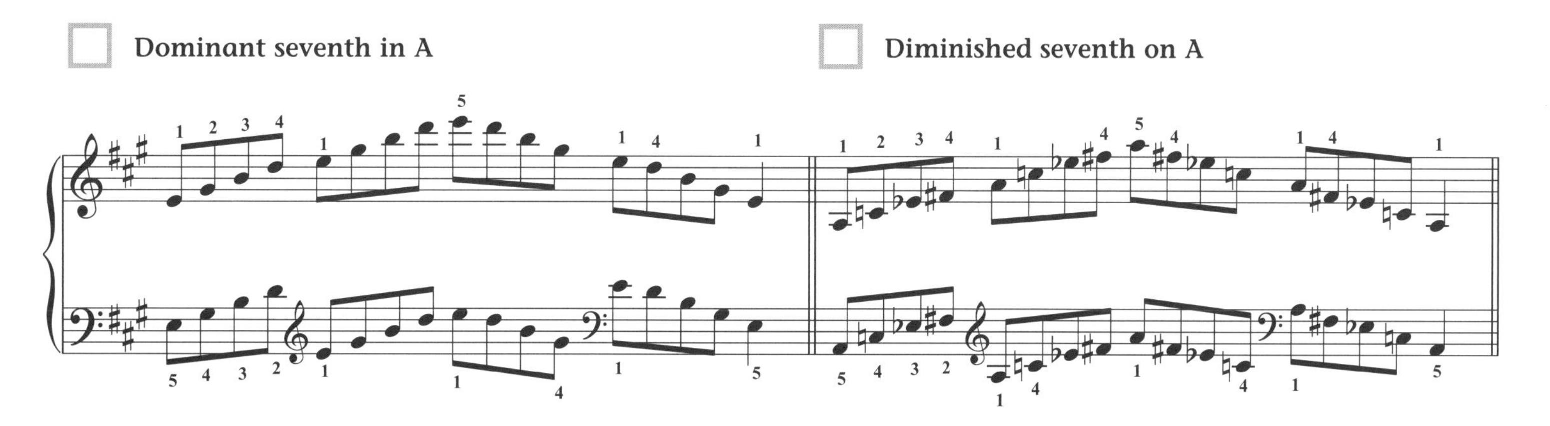

Hints and tips

- Scales in double thirds can be fingered in many ways; the system adopted here is the 'two group' fingering. Each octave is divided into a 3-note and 4-note group, the longer group using the gliding thumb.
- As well as practising using different variations of touch, tone, rhythm and range, you could try playing scales and arpeggios in keys related to A major: the relative minor (F♯ minor), the dominant (E major), the subdominant (D major) and the tonic minor (A minor).
- Using the 3rd finger where 4th is stipulated in arpeggios is accepted by some pianists, but it is better to train the weaker 4th finger from the earliest lessons to encourage proper, systematic hand shape development.

A minor

The relative major of A minor is C major.
Watch out for the raised seventh in A minor: G♯.

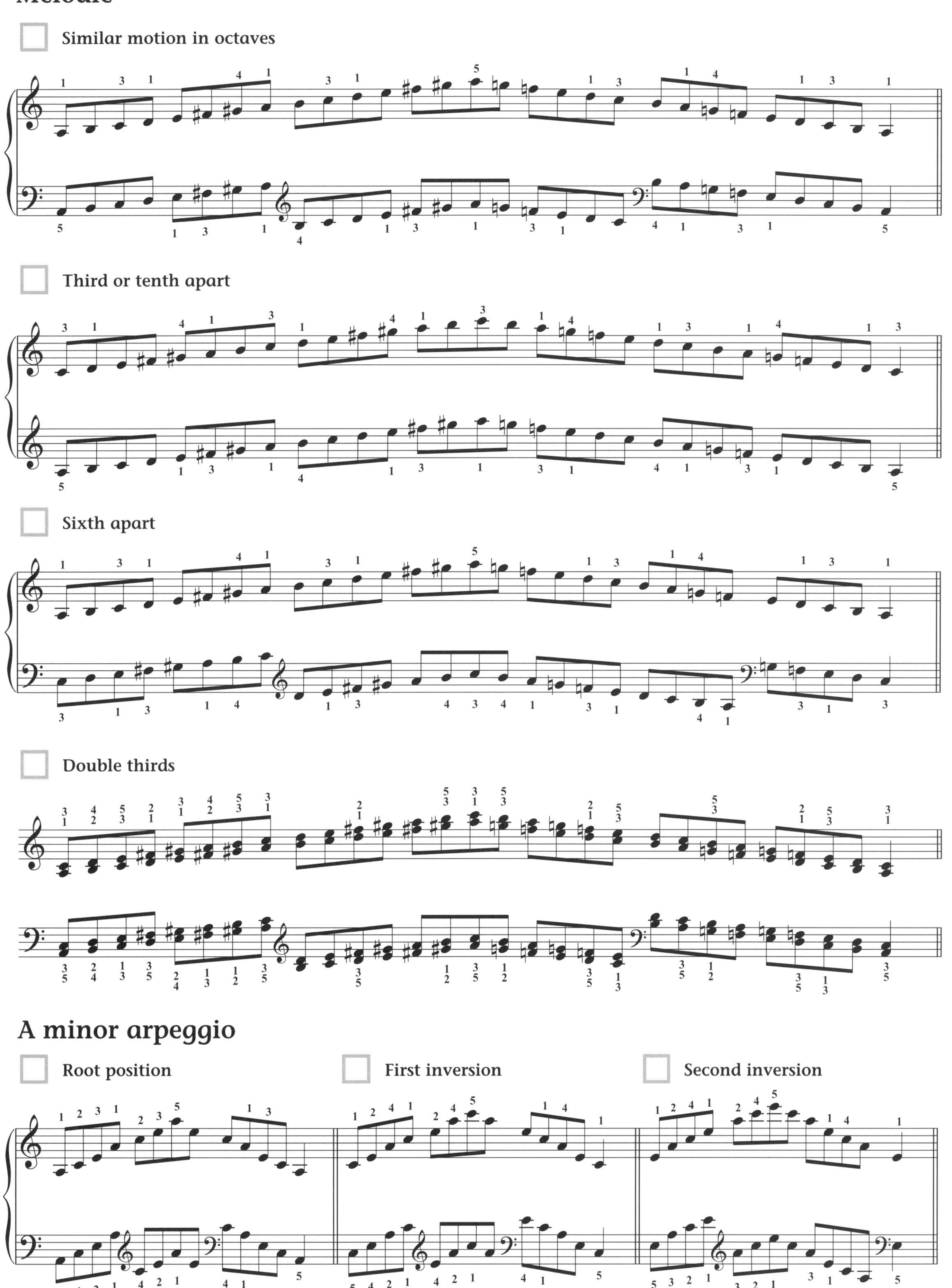
Melodic
Similar motion in octaves
Third or tenth apart
Sixth apart
Double thirds
A minor arpeggio
Root position
First inversion
Second inversion

E major

The relative minor of E major is C♯ minor.

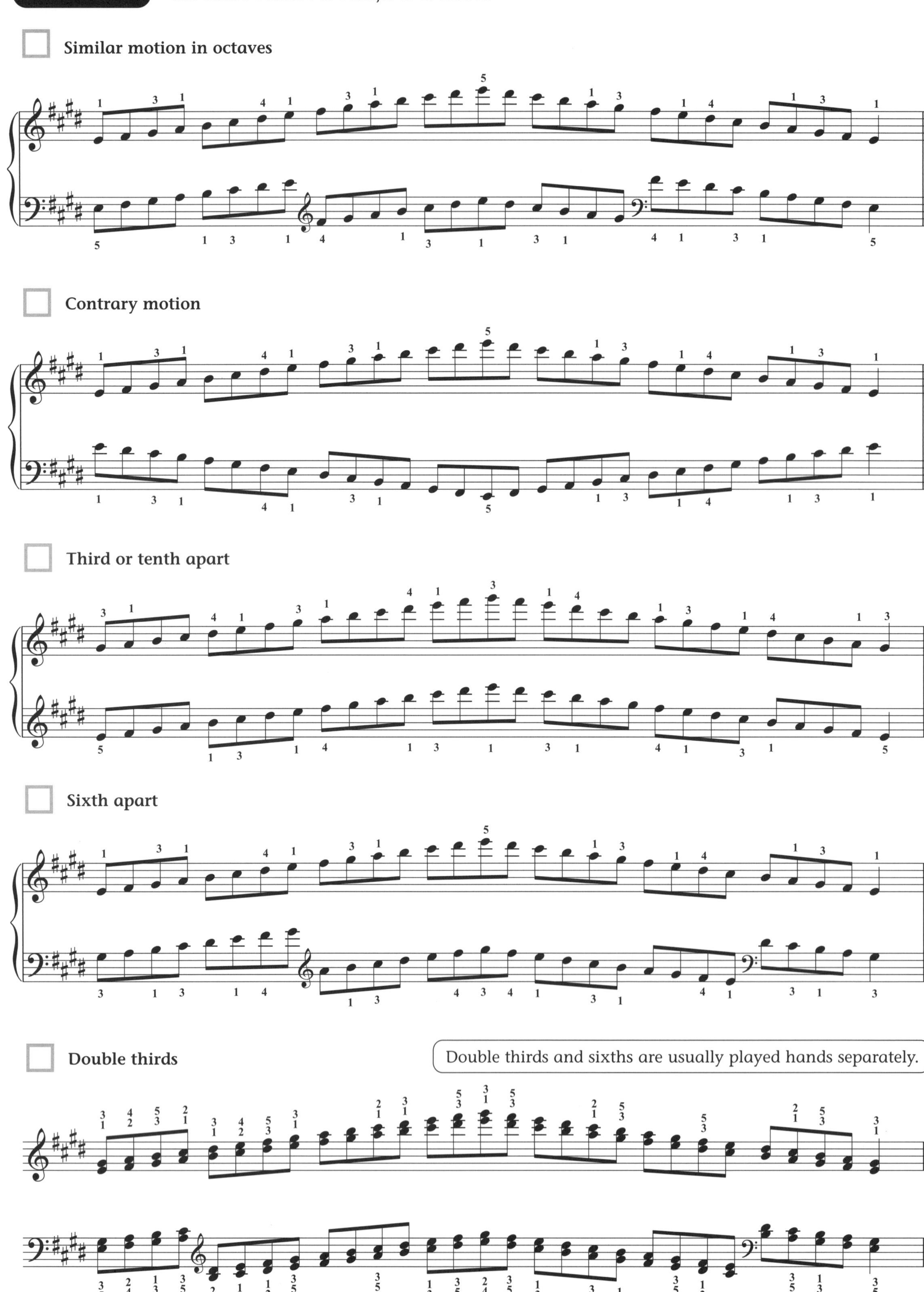

E major arpeggio

Root position

First inversion

Second inversion

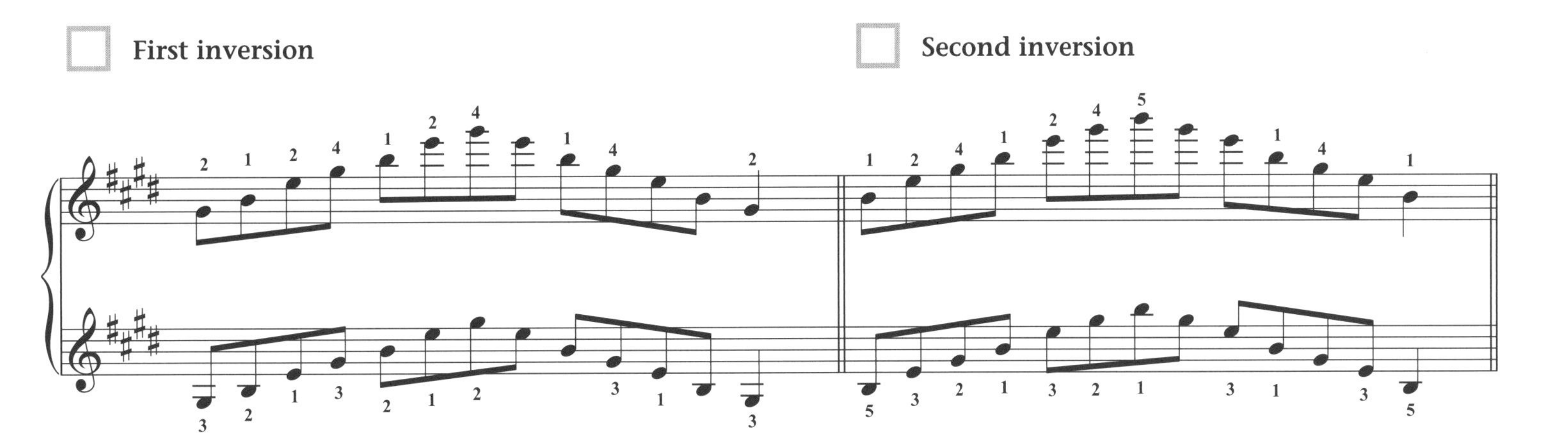

Dominant and diminished sevenths

Dominant seventh in E

Diminished seventh on E

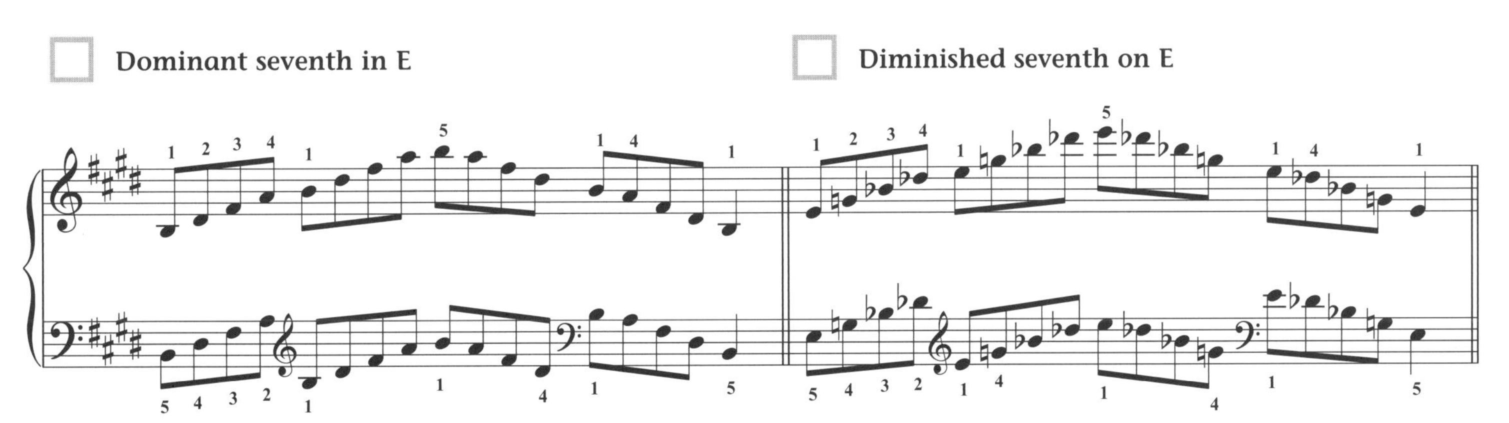

Hints and tips

- Scales in double thirds can be fingered in many ways; the system adopted here is the ‘two group’ fingering. Each octave is divided into a 3-note and 4-note group, the longer group using the gliding thumb.
- As well as practising using different variations of touch, tone, rhythm and range, you could try playing scales and arpeggios in keys related to E major: the relative minor (C♯ minor), the dominant (B major), the subdominant (A major) and the tonic minor (E minor).
- Using the 3rd finger where 4th is stipulated in arpeggios is accepted by some pianists, but it is better to train the weaker 4th finger from the earliest lessons to encourage proper, systematic hand shape development.

E minor

The relative major of E minor is G major.
Watch out for the raised seventh in E minor: D♯.

Harmonic

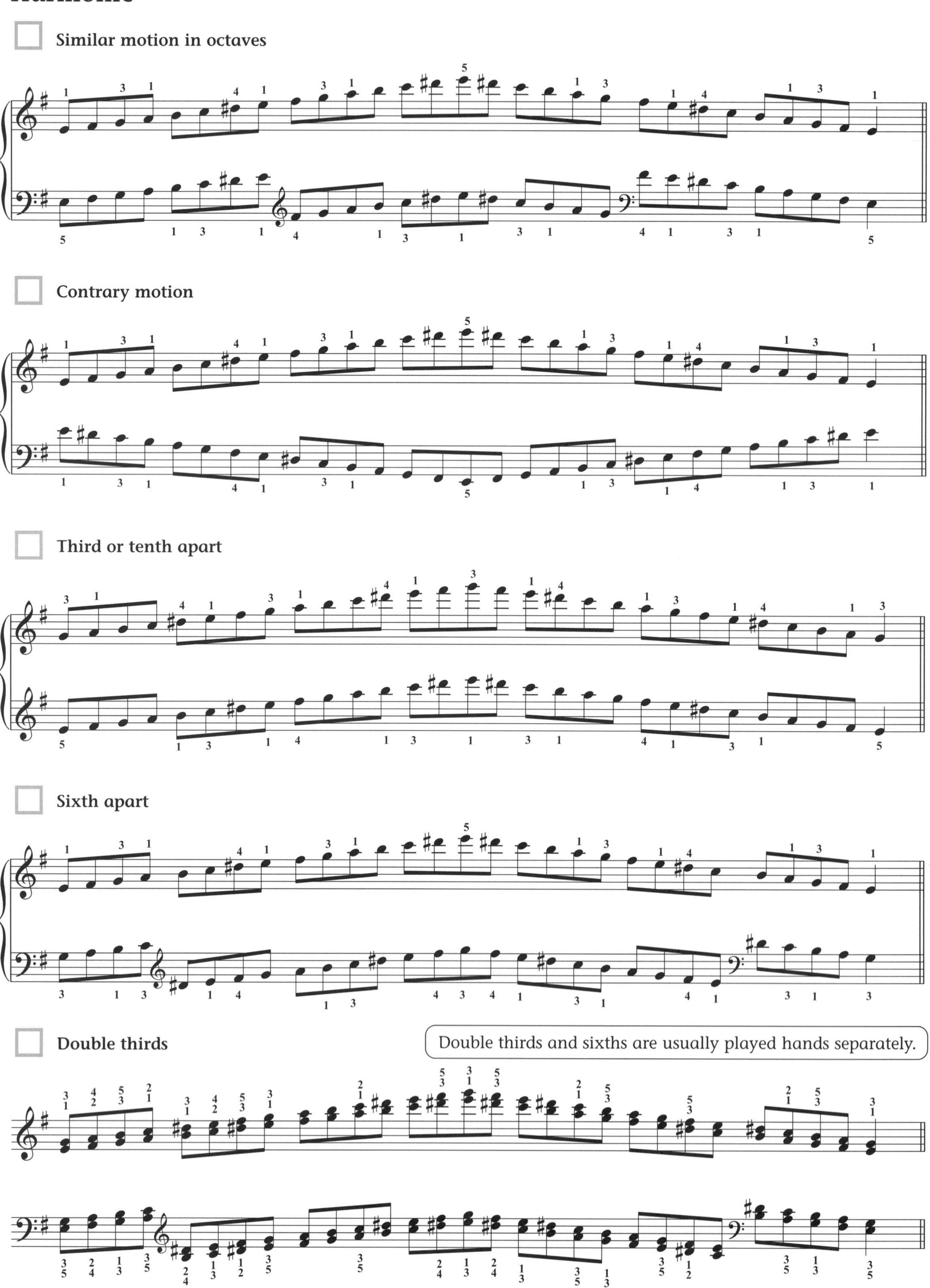

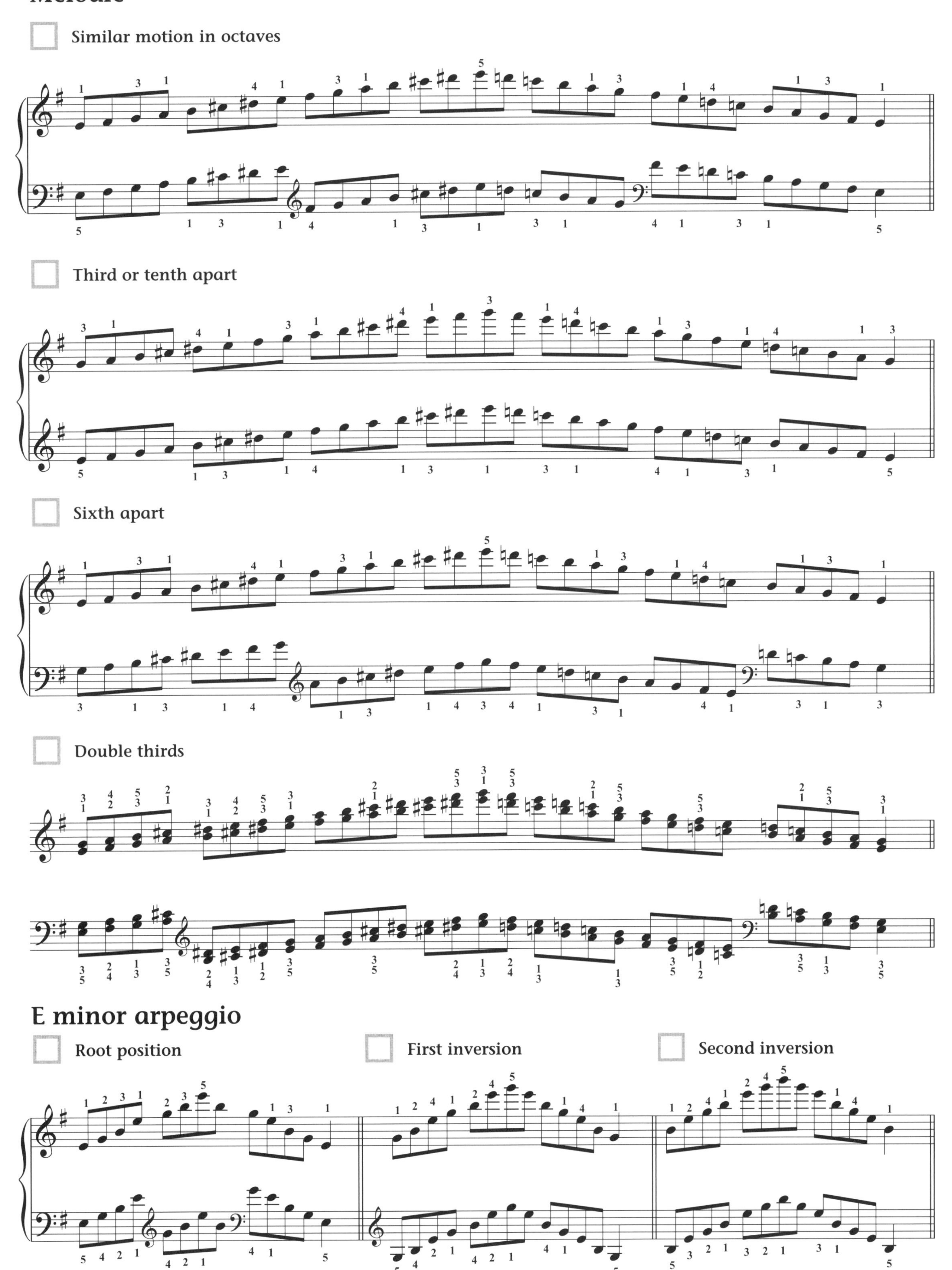
Melodic
Similar motion in octaves
Third or tenth apart
Sixth apart
Double thirds
E minor arpeggio
Root position
First inversion
Second inversion

B major

The relative minor of B major is G♯ minor.

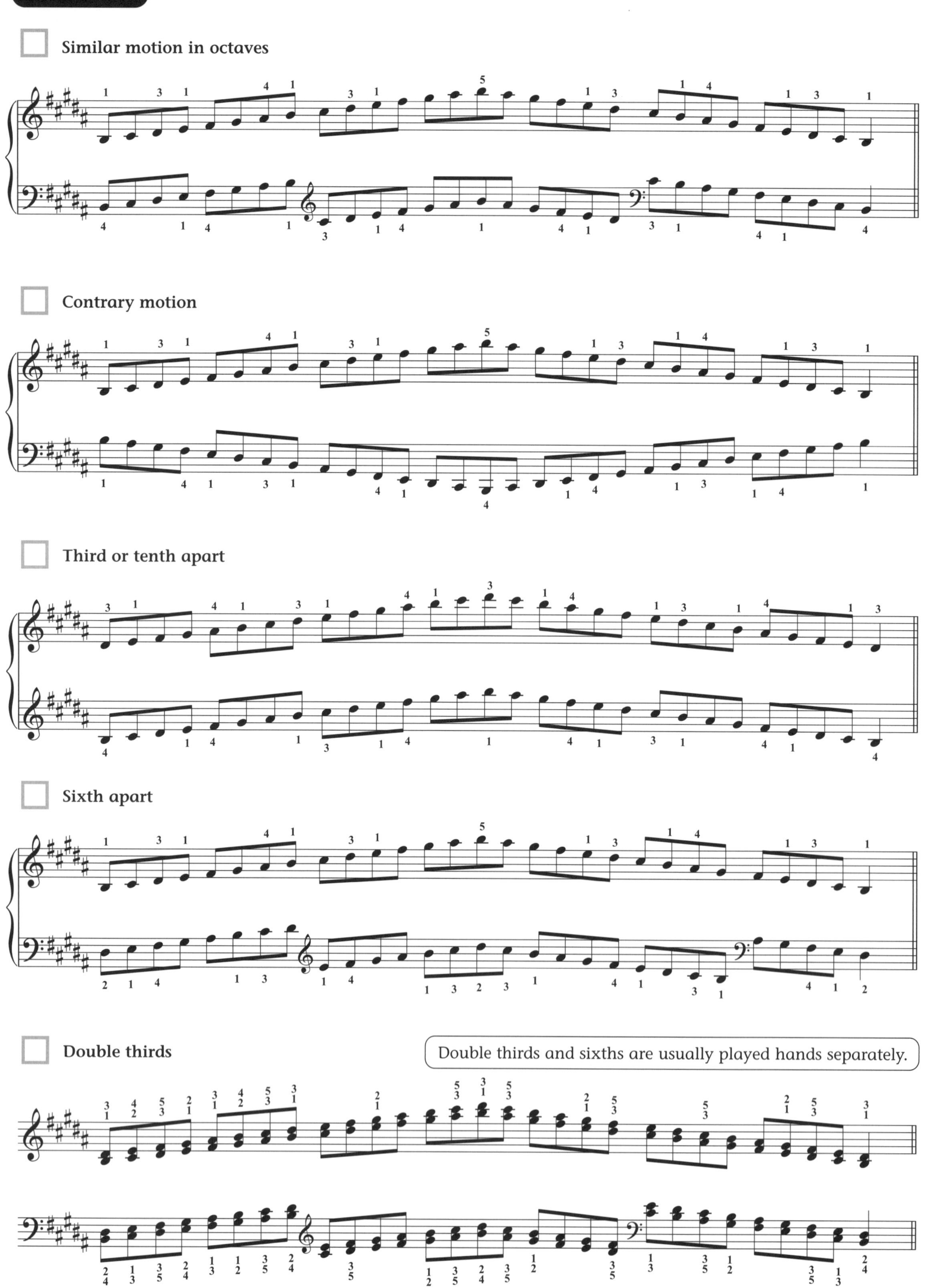

B major arpeggio

Root position

First inversion

Second inversion

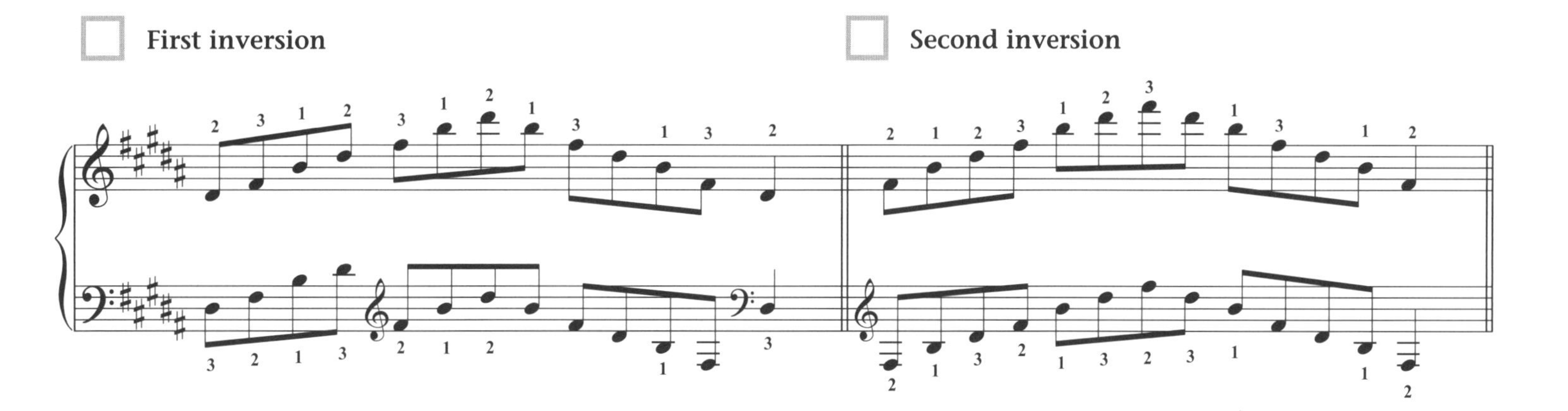

Dominant and diminished sevenths

Dominant seventh in B

Diminished seventh on B

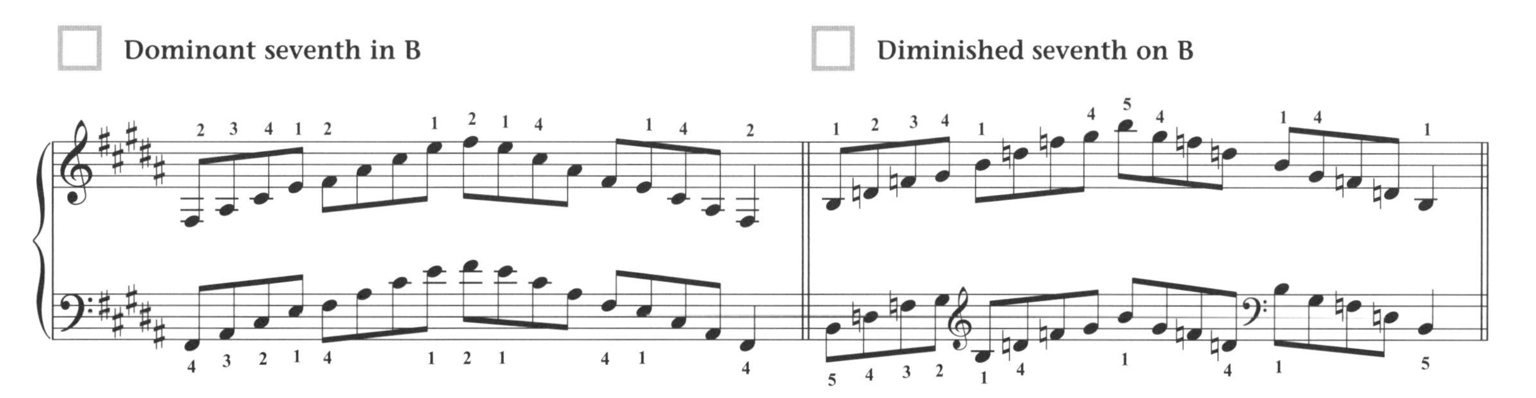

Hints and tips

- Scales in double thirds can be fingered in many ways; the system adopted here is the 'two group' fingering. Each octave is divided into a 3-note and 4-note group, the longer group using the gliding thumb.
- As well as practising using different variations of touch, tone, rhythm and range, you could try playing scales and arpeggios in keys related to B major: the relative minor (G♯ minor), the dominant (F♯ major), the subdominant (E major) and the tonic minor (B minor).
- Using the 3rd finger where 4th is stipulated in arpeggios is accepted by some pianists, but it is better to train the weaker 4th finger from the earliest lessons to encourage proper, systematic hand shape development.

B minor

The relative major of B minor is D major.
Watch out for the raised seventh in B minor: A♯.

Harmonic

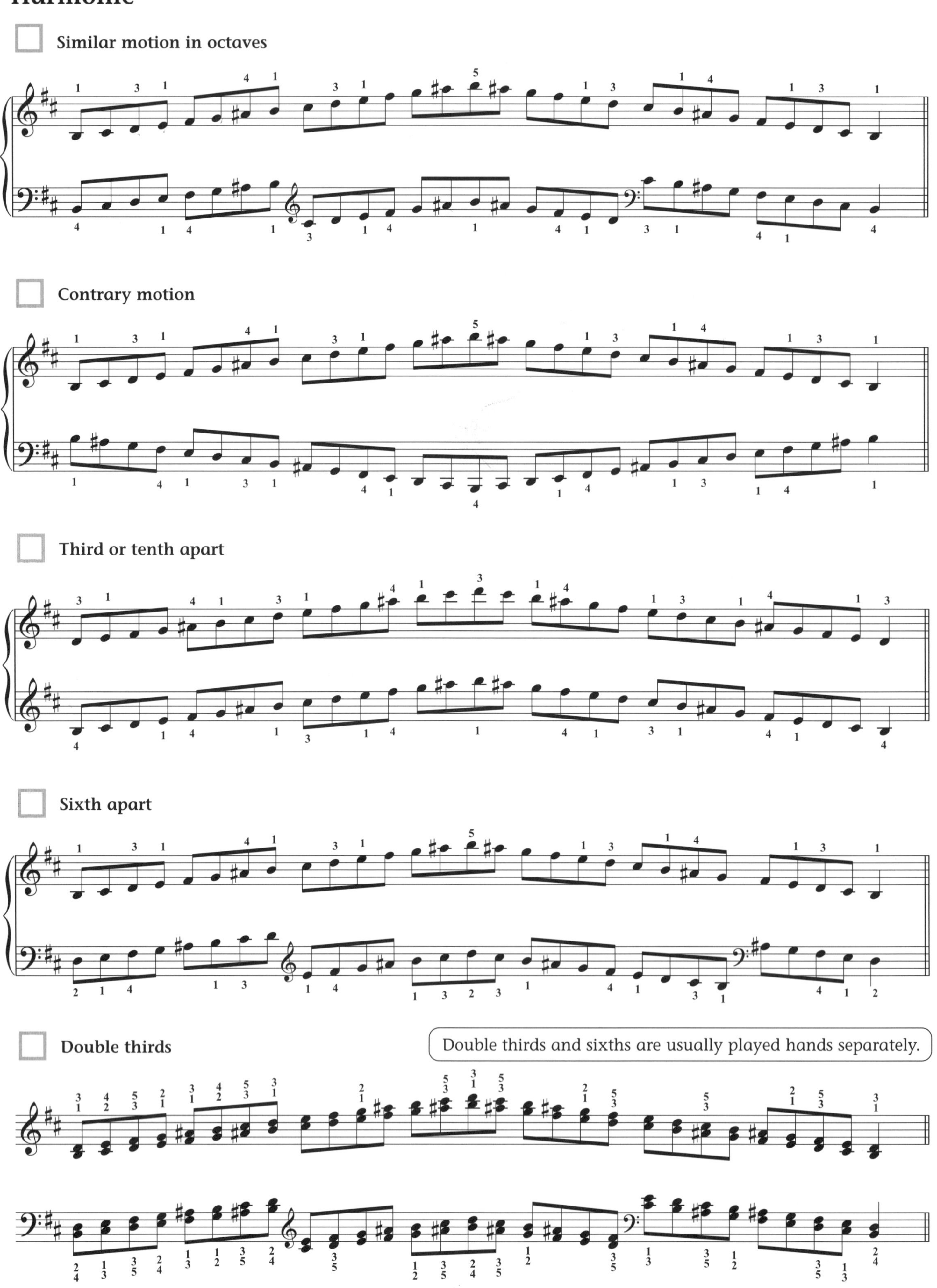

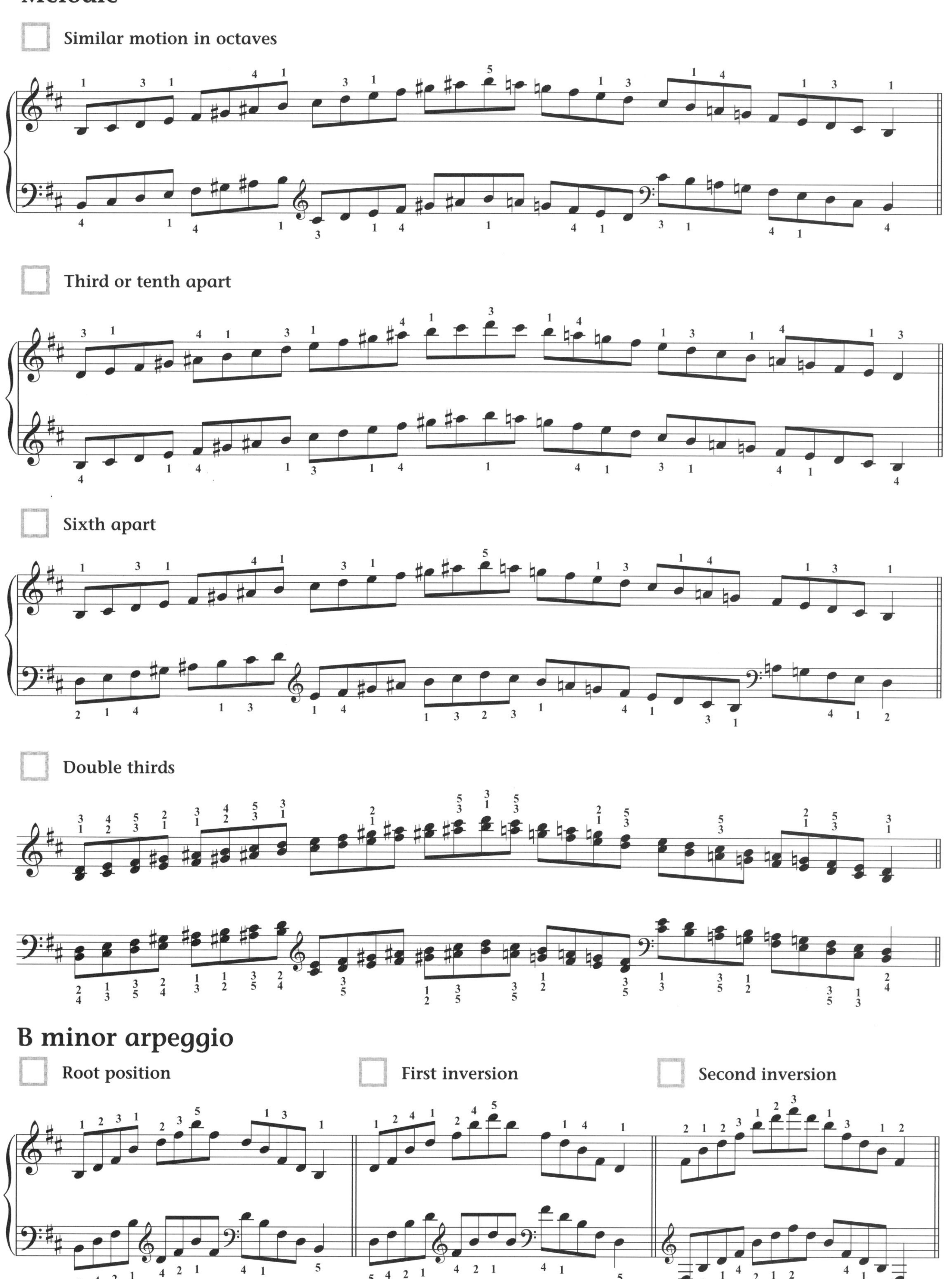
Melodic
Similar motion in octaves
Third or tenth apart
Sixth apart
Double thirds
B minor arpeggio
Root position
First inversion
Second inversion

F♯ major

The relative minor of F♯ major is D♯ (enharmonic E♭) minor.

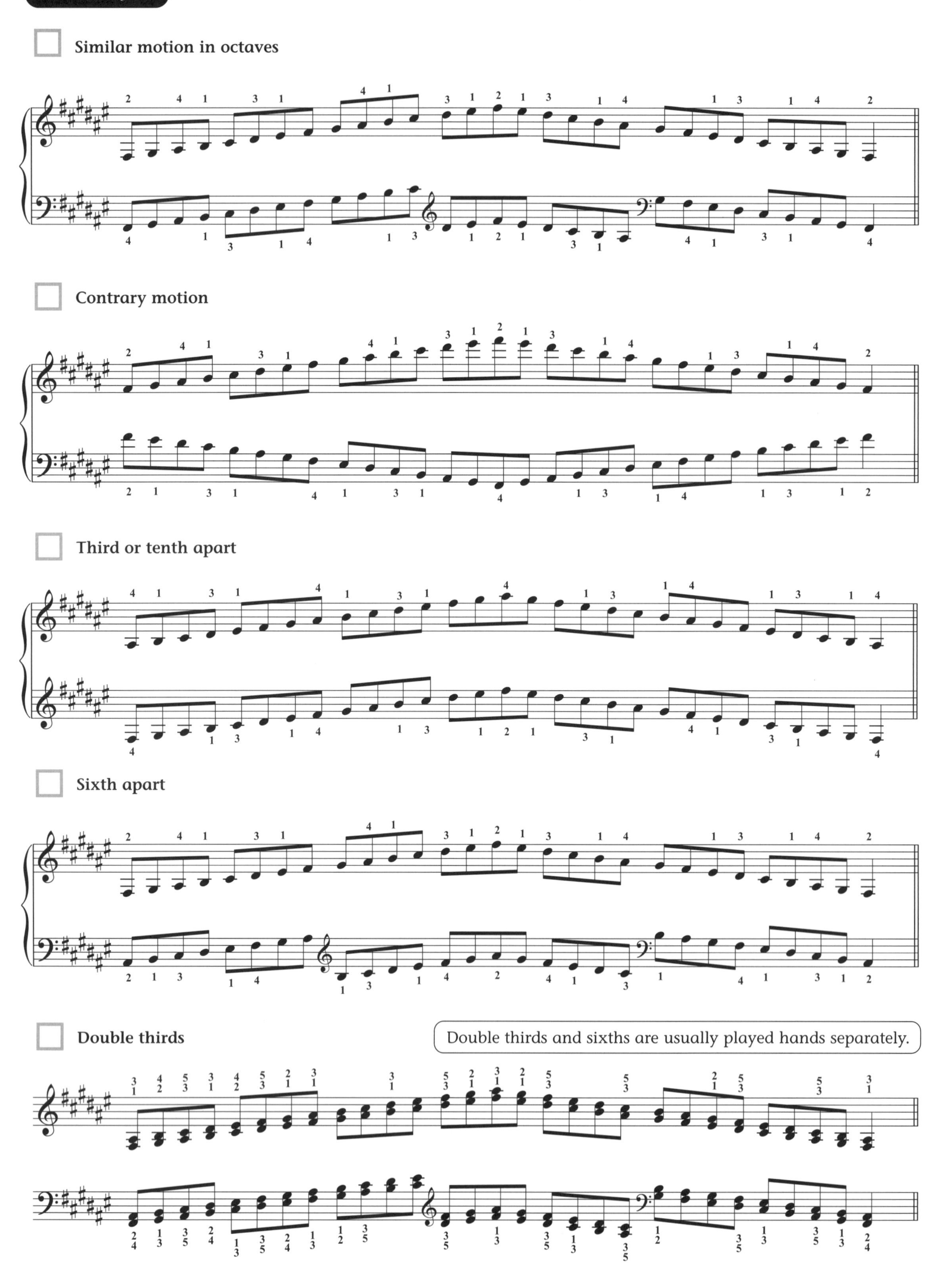

F♯ major arpeggio

☐ Root position

☐ First inversion

☐ Second inversion

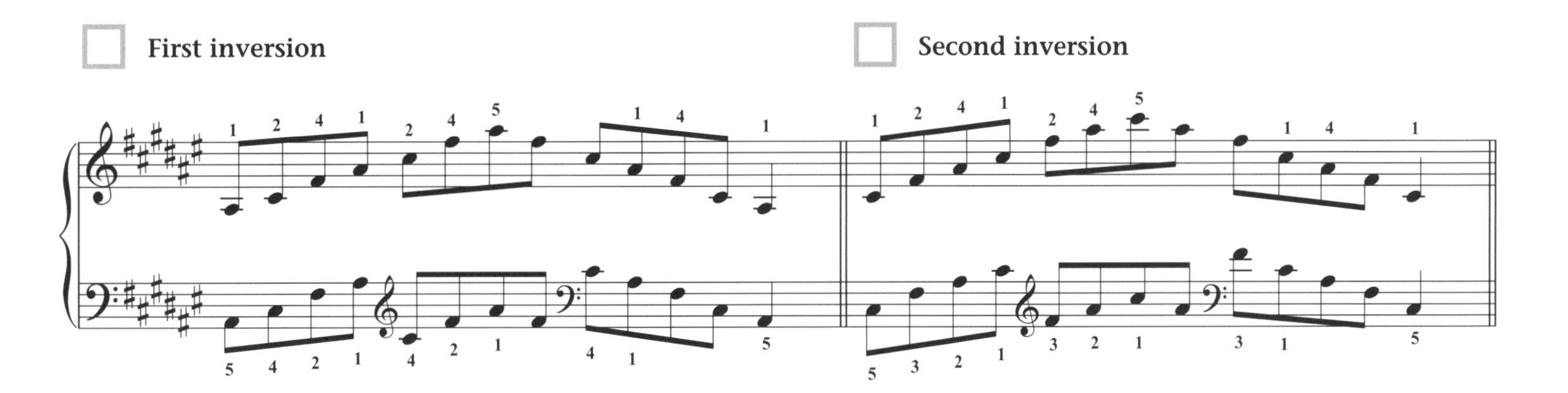

Dominant and diminished sevenths

☐ Dominant seventh in F♯

☐ Diminished seventh on F♯

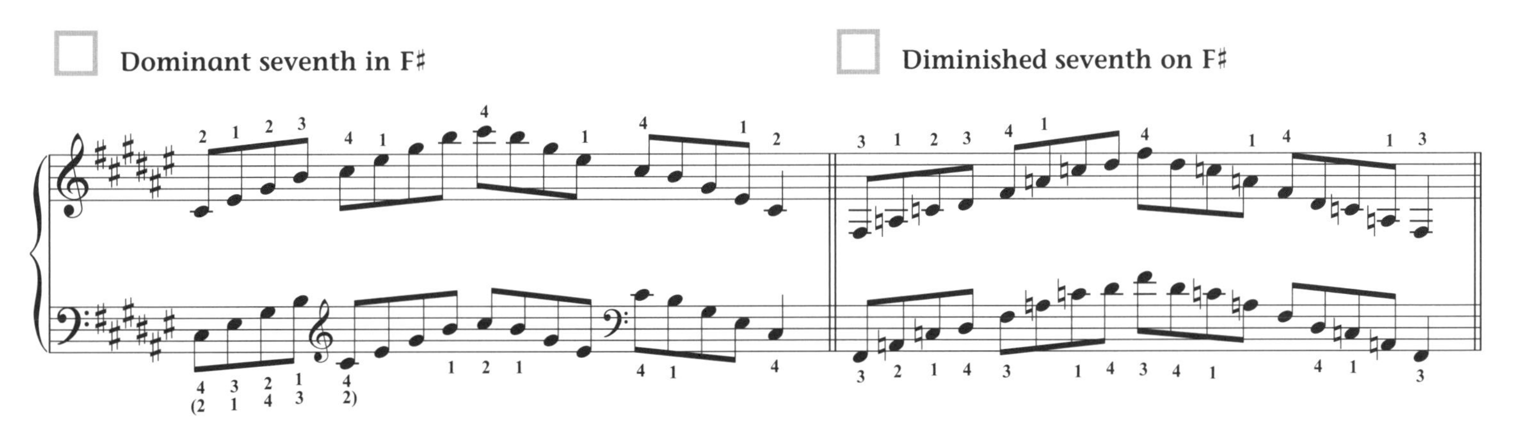

Hints and tips

- Scales in double thirds can be fingered in many ways; the system adopted here is the 'two group' fingering. Each octave is divided into a 3-note and 4-note group, the longer group using the gliding thumb.
- As well as practising using different variations of touch, tone, rhythm and range, you could try playing scales and arpeggios in keys related to F♯ major: the relative minor (D♯ minor), the dominant (C♯/D♭ major), the subdominant (B major) and the tonic minor (F♯ minor).
- Using the 3rd finger where 4th is stipulated in arpeggios is accepted by some pianists, but it is better to train the weaker 4th finger from the earliest lessons to encourage proper, systematic hand shape development.

F♯ minor

The relative major of F♯ minor is A major.
Watch out for the raised seventh in F♯ minor: E♯.

Harmonic

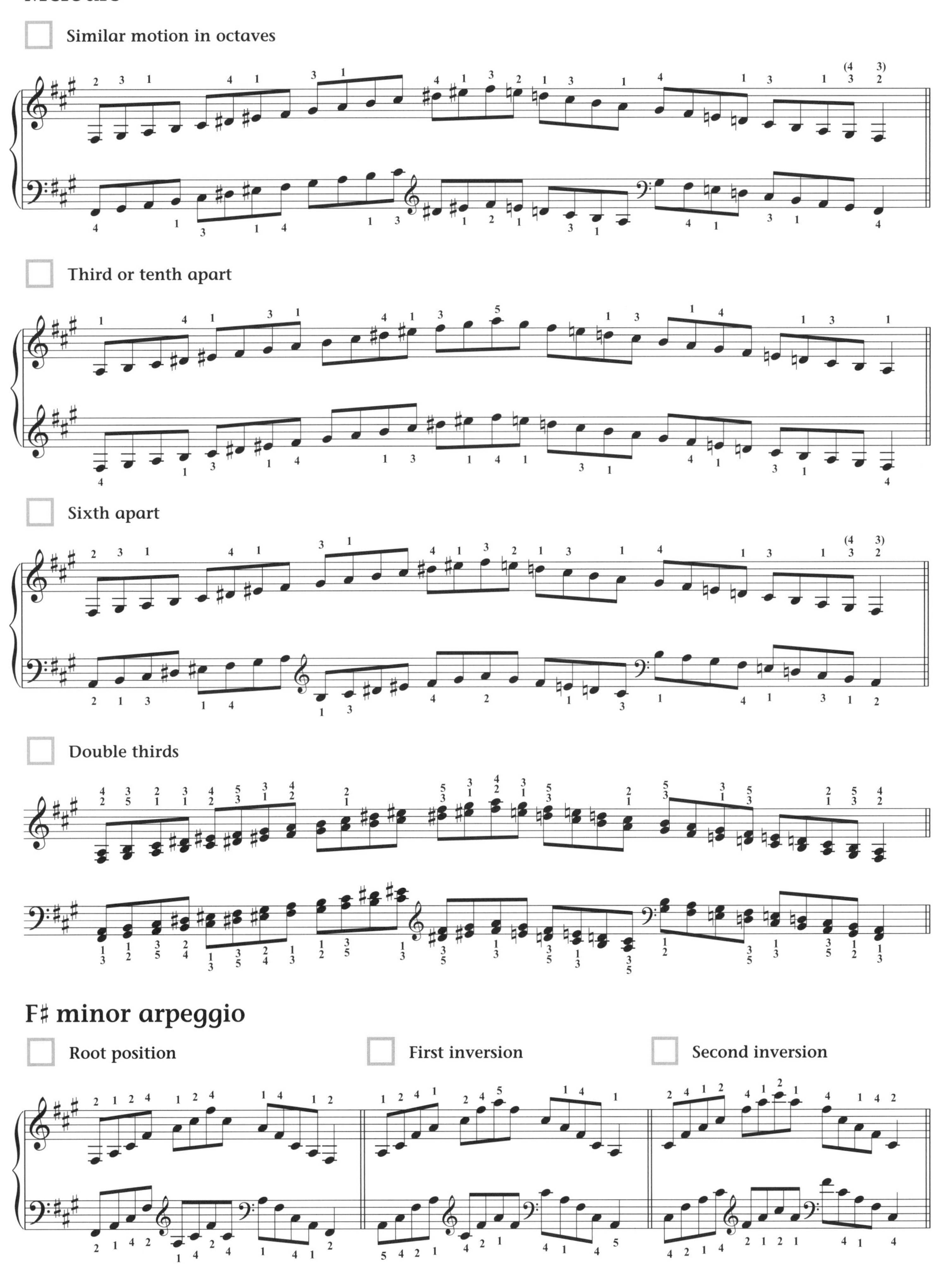
Melodic
Similar motion in octaves
Third or tenth apart
Sixth apart
Double thirds
F♯ minor arpeggio
Root position
First inversion
Second inversion

D♭ major

The relative minor of D♭ major is B♭ minor.

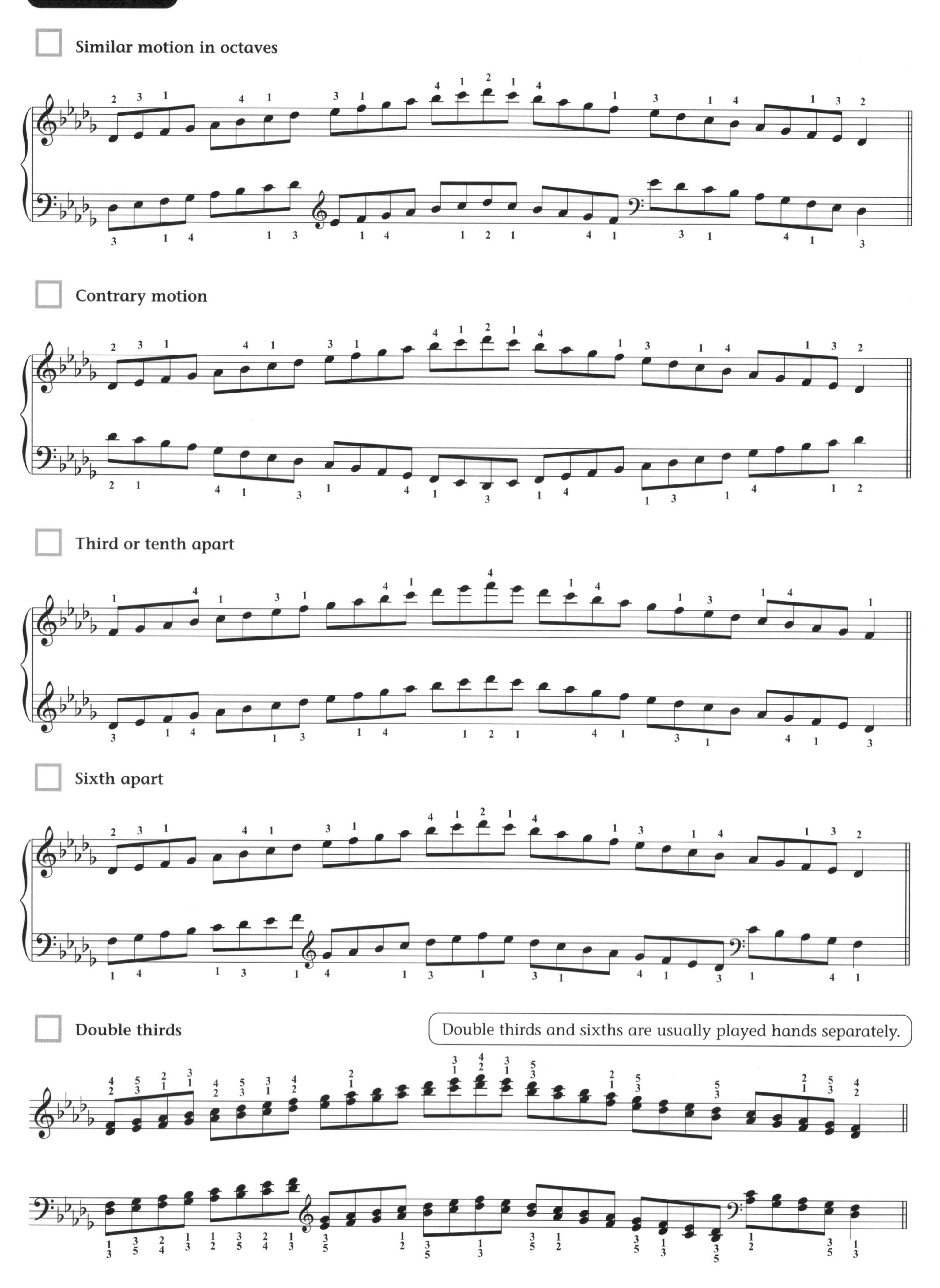

D♭ major arpeggio

☐ Root position

☐ First inversion

☐ Second inversion

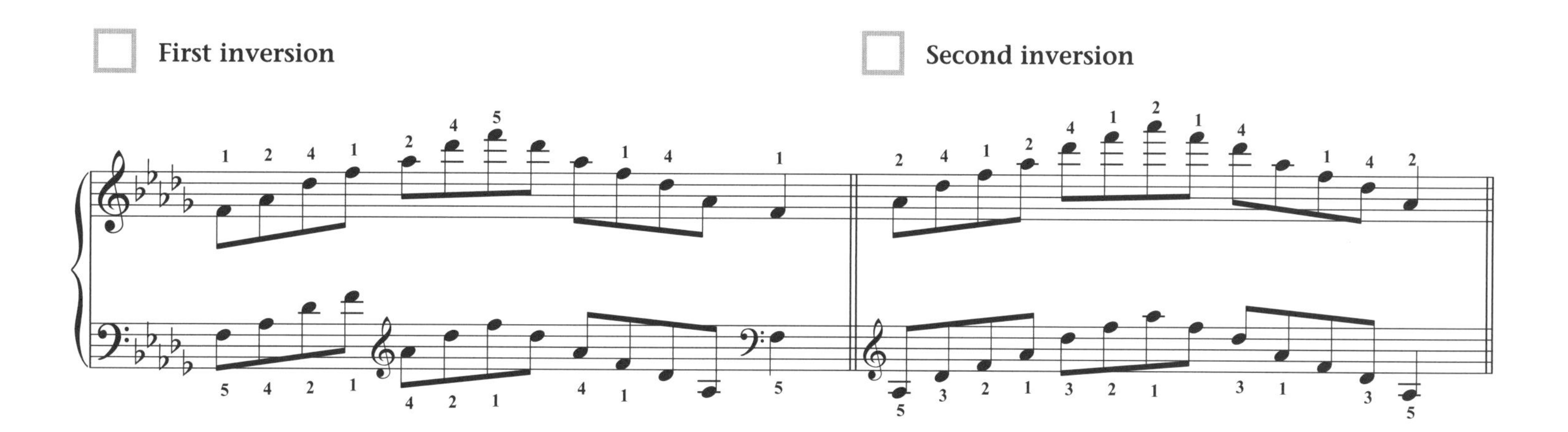

Dominant and diminished sevenths

☐ Dominant seventh in D♭

☐ Diminished seventh on C♯

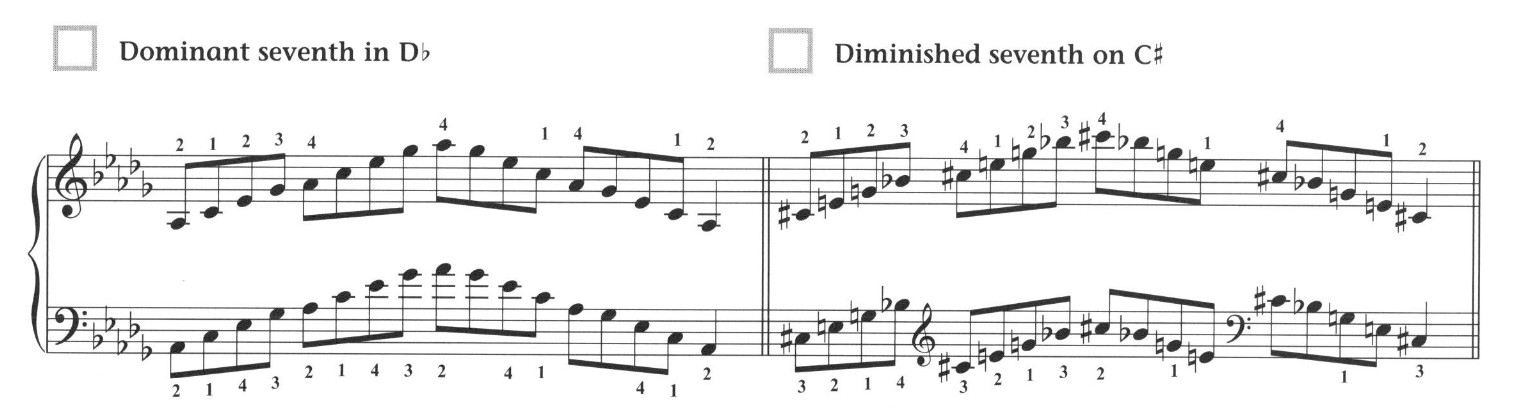

Hints and tips

- Scales in double thirds can be fingered in many ways; the system adopted here is the 'two group' fingering. Each octave is divided into a 3-note and 4-note group, the longer group using the gliding thumb.
- As well as practising using different variations of touch, tone, rhythm and range, you could try playing scales and arpeggios in keys related to D♭ major: the relative minor (B♭ minor), the dominant (A♭ major), the subdominant (G♭/F♯ major) and the tonic minor (D♭/C♯ minor).
- Using the 3rd finger where 4th is stipulated in arpeggios is accepted by some pianists, but it is better to train the weaker 4th finger from the earliest lessons to encourage proper, systematic hand shape development.

C♯ minor

The relative major of C♯ minor is E major.
Watch out for the raised seventh in C♯ minor: B♯.

Harmonic

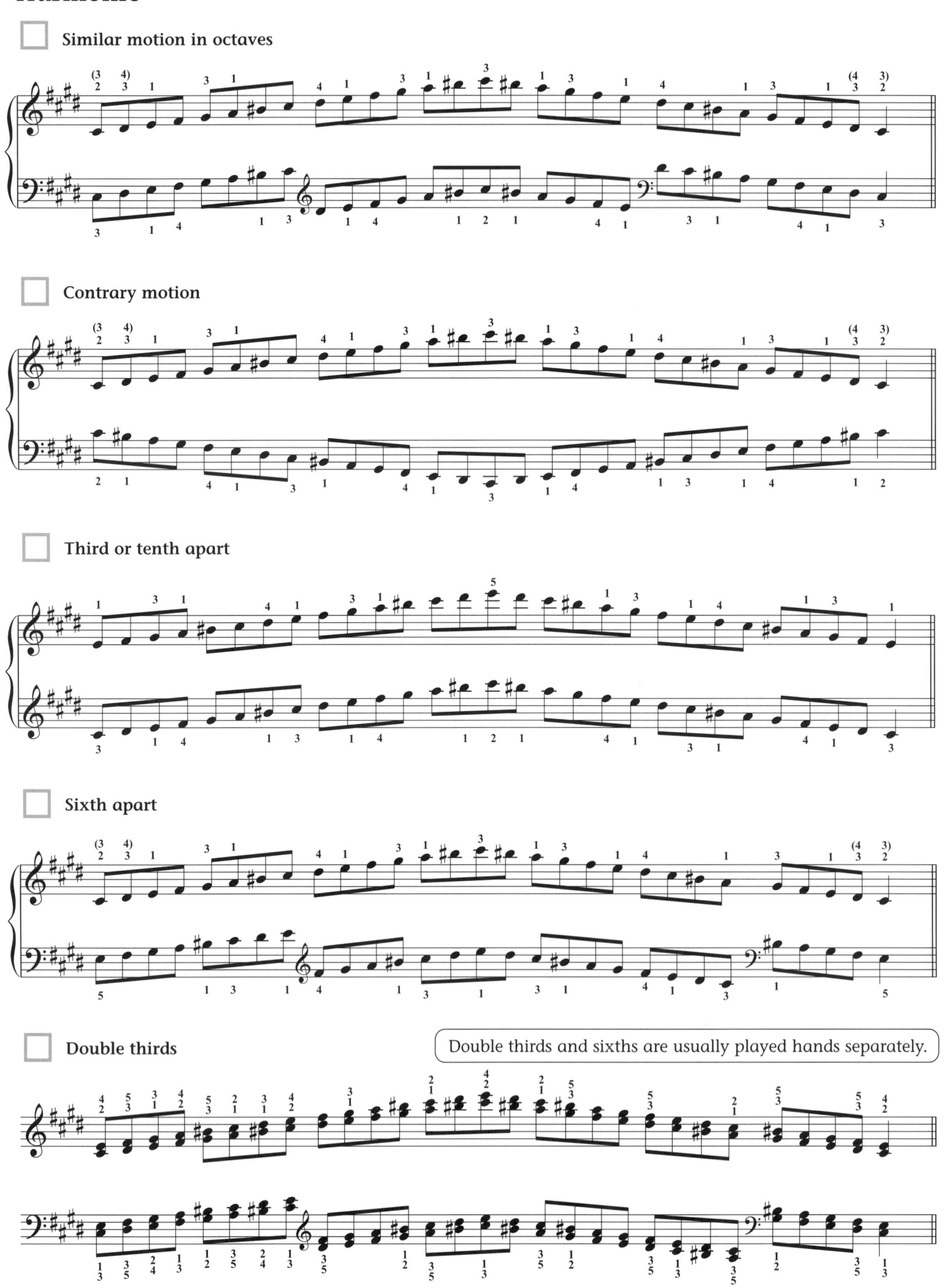

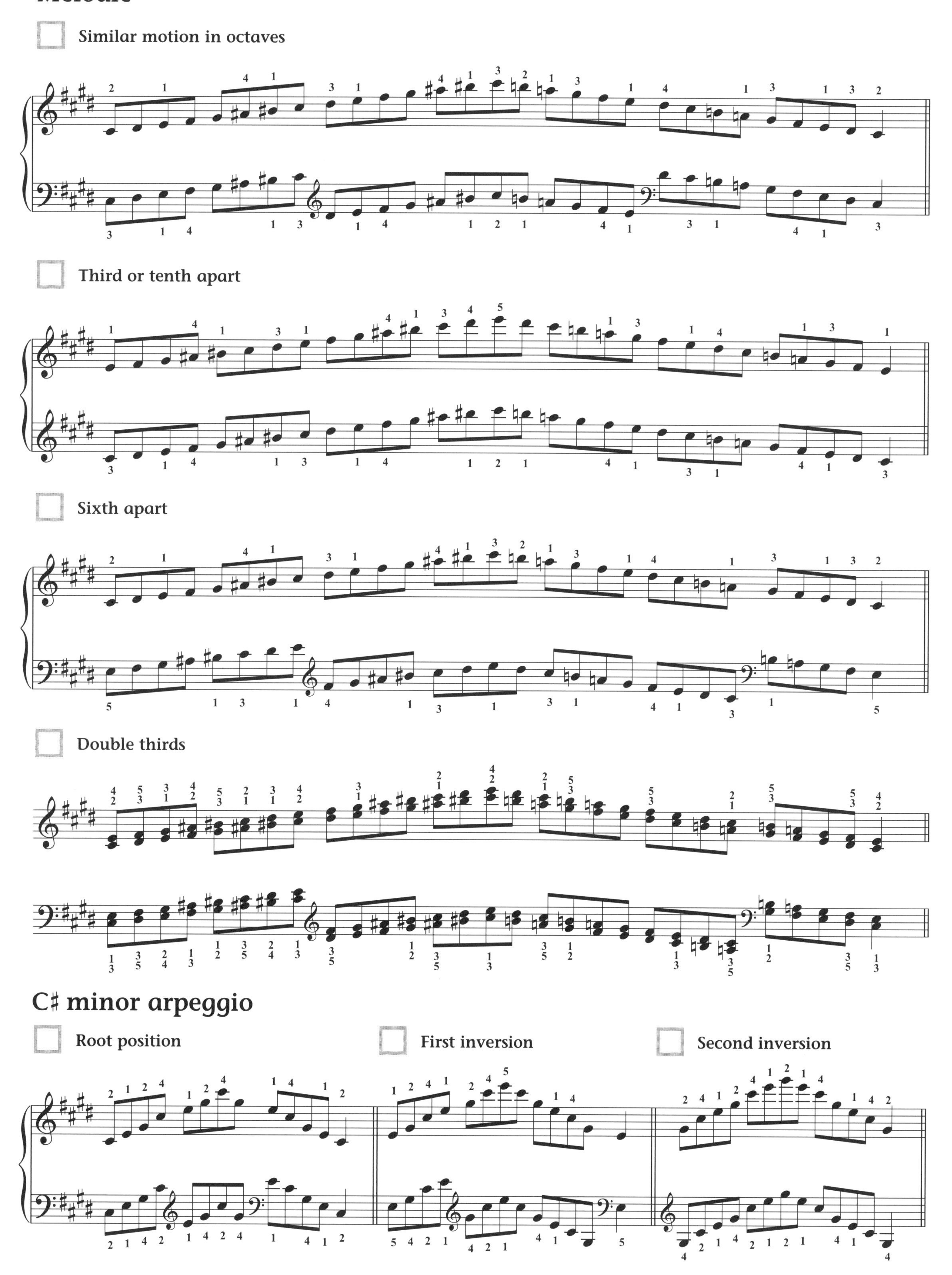
Melodic
Similar motion in octaves
Third or tenth apart
Sixth apart
Double thirds
C♯ minor arpeggio
Root position
First inversion
Second inversion

A♭ major

The relative minor of A♭ major is F minor.

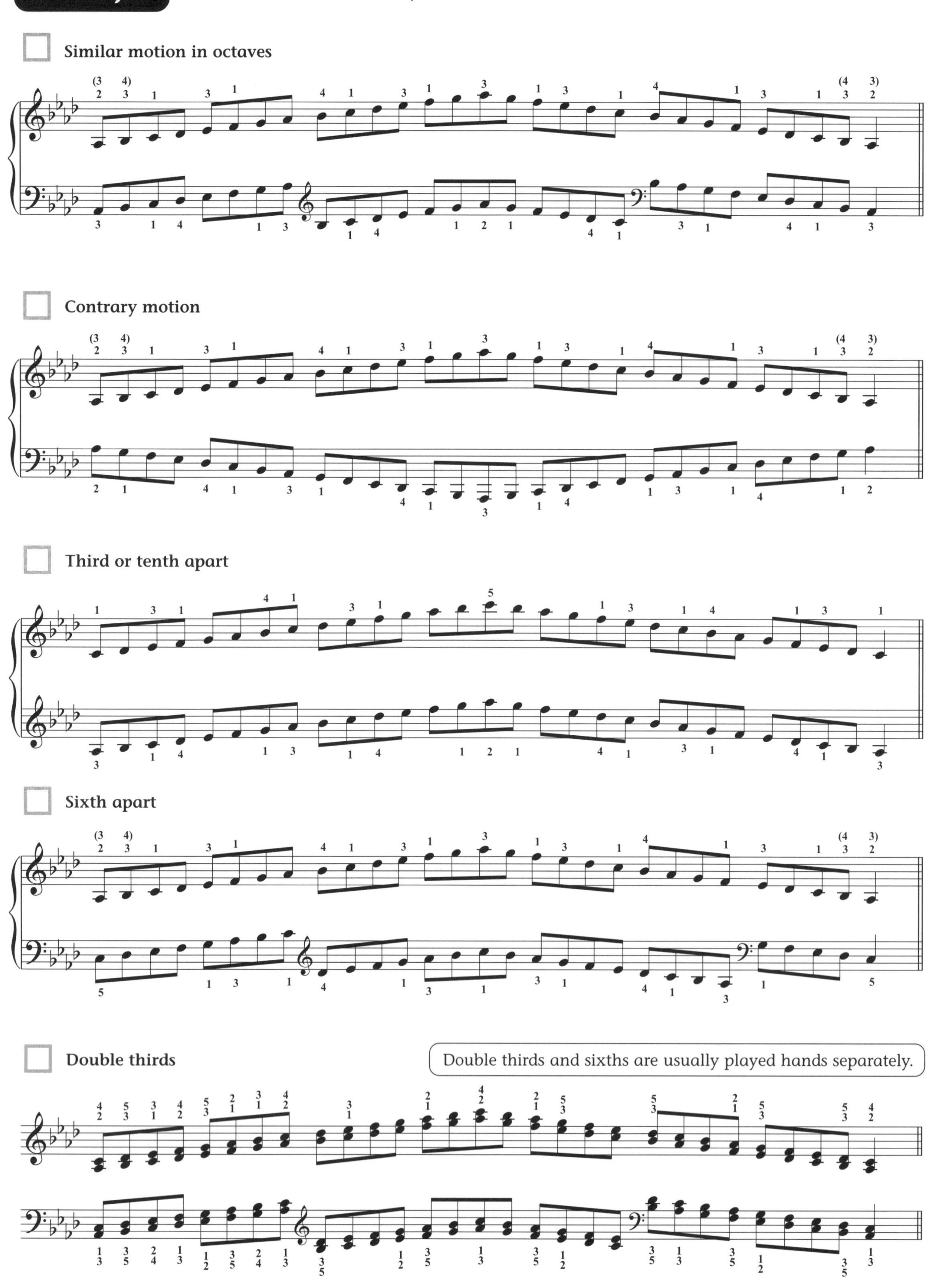

A♭ major arpeggio

☐ Root position

☐ First inversion ☐ Second inversion

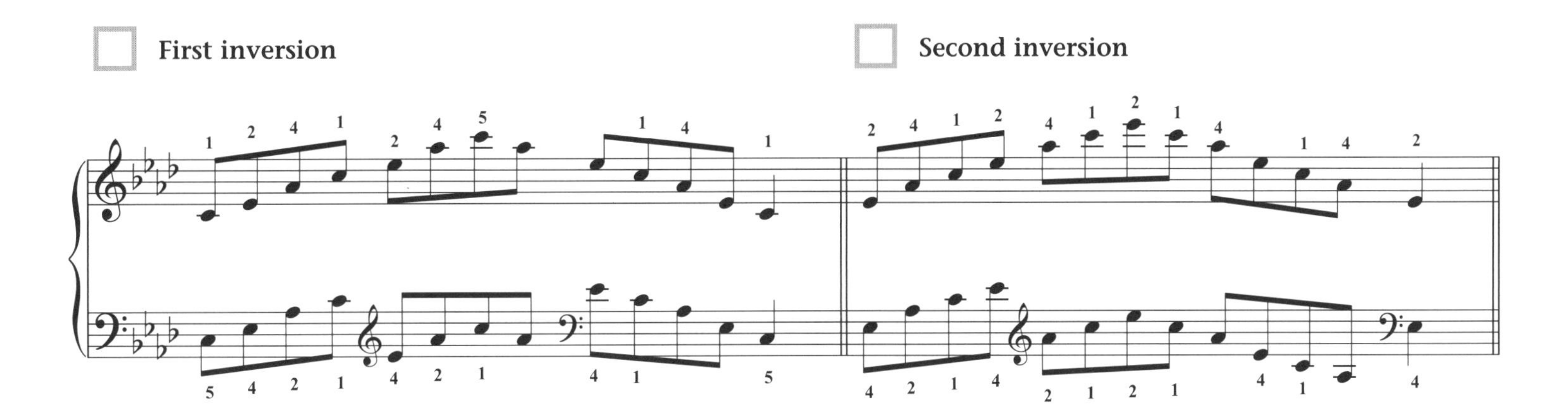

Dominant and diminished sevenths

☐ Dominant seventh in A♭ ☐ Diminished seventh on A♭

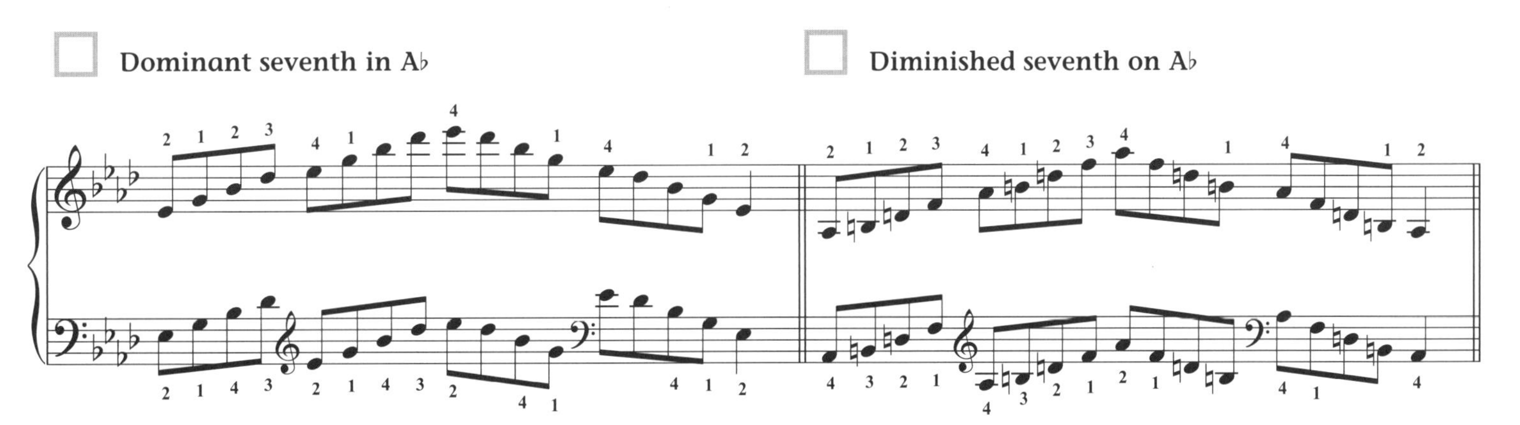

Hints and tips

- Scales in double thirds can be fingered in many ways; the system adopted here is the 'two group' fingering. Each octave is divided into a 3-note and 4-note group, the longer group using the gliding thumb.
- As well as practising using different variations of touch, tone, rhythm and range, you could try playing scales and arpeggios in keys related to A♭ major: the relative minor (F minor), the dominant (E♭ major), the subdominant (D♭ major) and the tonic minor (A♭/G♯ minor).
- Using the 3rd finger where 4th is stipulated in arpeggios is accepted by some pianists, but it is better to train the weaker 4th finger from the earliest lessons to encourage proper, systematic hand shape development.

G♯ minor

The relative major of G♯ minor is B major.
Watch out for the raised seventh in G♯ minor: F𝄪.

Harmonic

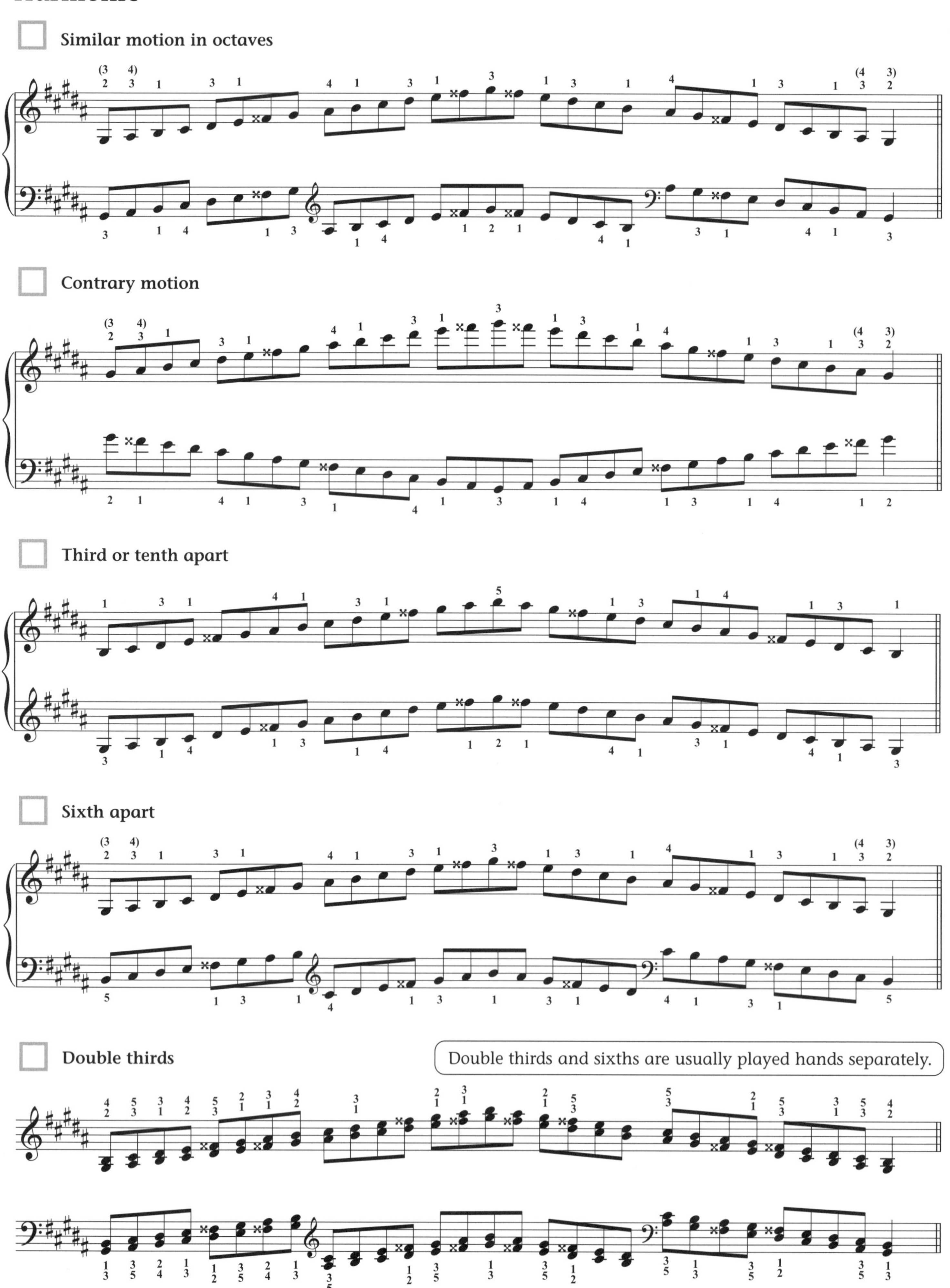

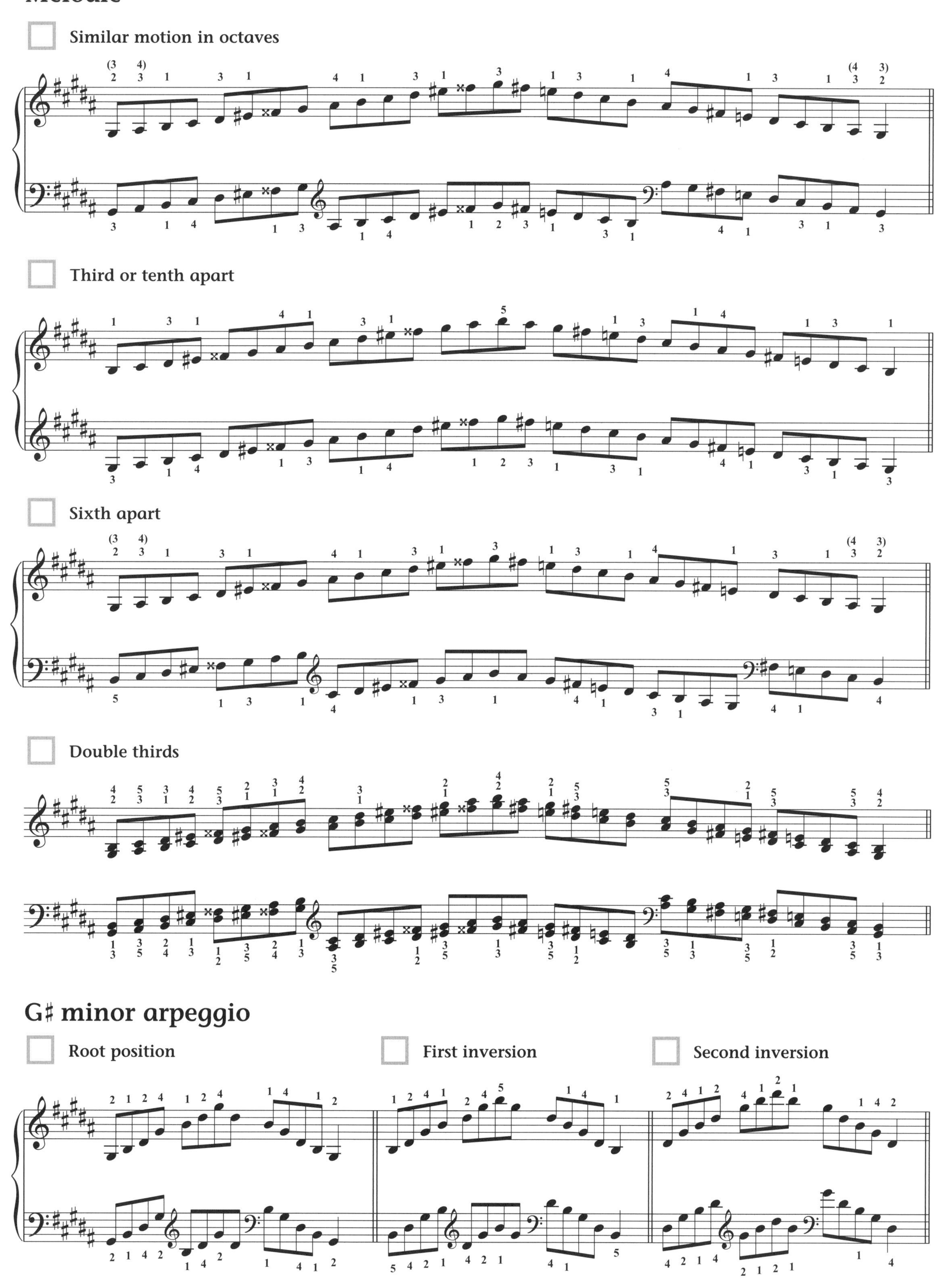
Melodic
Similar motion in octaves
Third or tenth apart
Sixth apart
Double thirds
G♯ minor arpeggio
Root position
First inversion
Second inversion

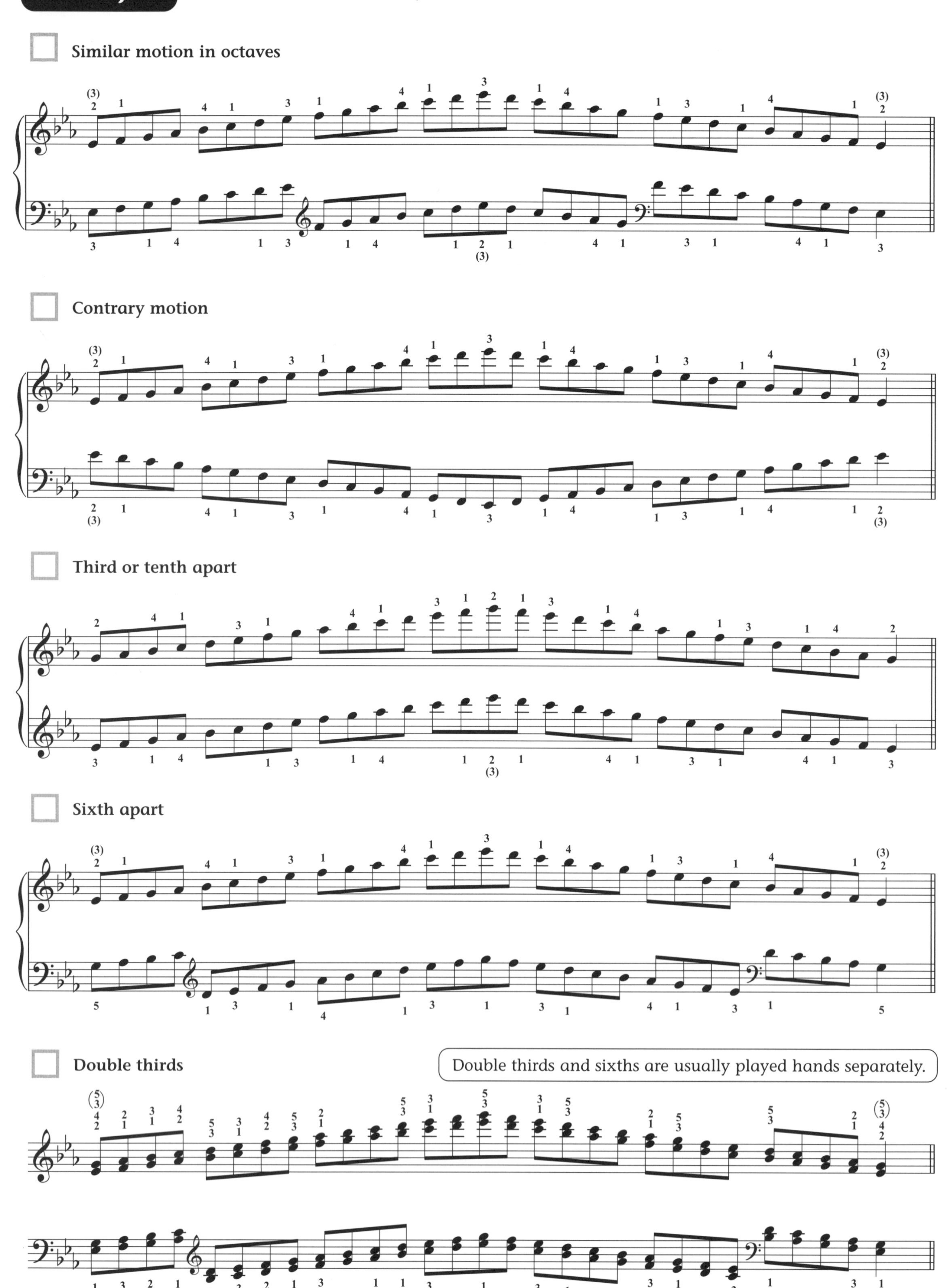
E♭ major
The relative minor of E♭ major is C minor.
Similar motion in octaves
Contrary motion
Third or tenth apart
Sixth apart
Double thirds
Double thirds and sixths are usually played hands separately.

E♭ major arpeggio

Root position

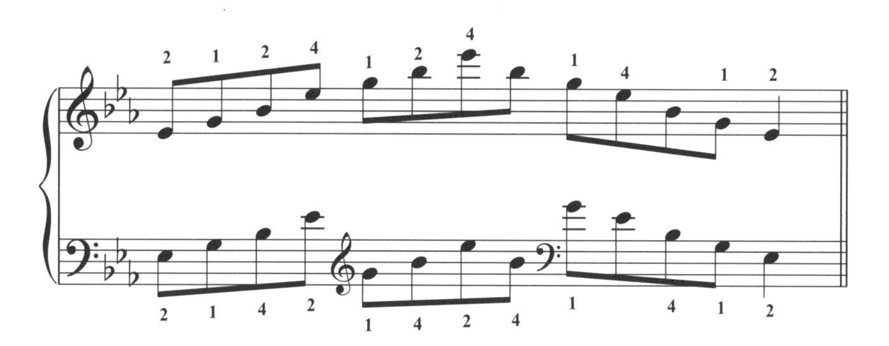

First inversion

Second inversion

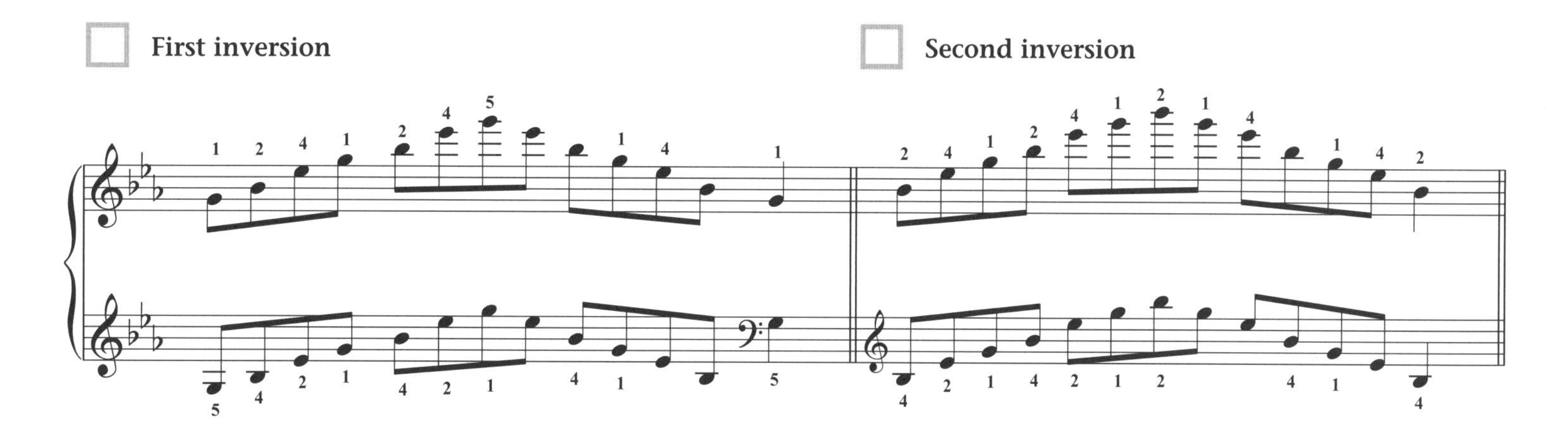

Dominant and diminished sevenths

Dominant seventh in E♭

Diminished seventh on E♭

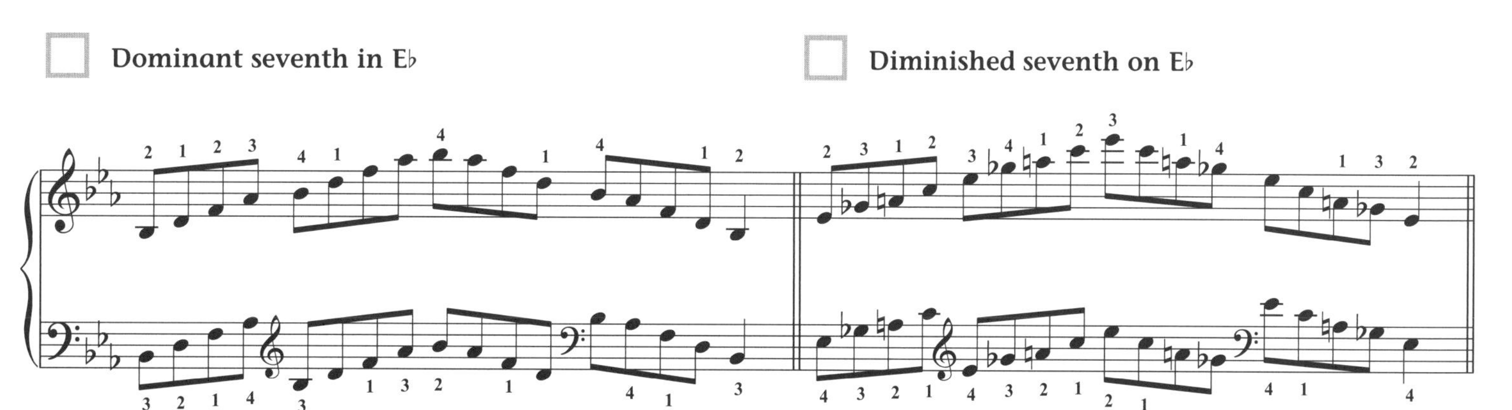

Hints and tips

- Scales in double thirds can be fingered in many ways; the system adopted here is the 'two group' fingering. Each octave is divided into a 3-note and 4-note group, the longer group using the gliding thumb.
- As well as practising using different variations of touch, tone, rhythm and range, you could try playing scales and arpeggios in keys related to E♭ major: the relative minor (C minor), the dominant (B♭ major), the subdominant (A♭ major) and the tonic minor (E♭ minor).
- Using the 3rd finger where 4th is stipulated in arpeggios is accepted by some pianists, but it is better to train the weaker 4th finger from the earliest lessons to encourage proper, systematic hand shape development.

E♭ minor

The relative major of E♭ minor is G♭ (enharmonic F♯) major.
Watch out for the raised seventh in E♭ minor: D♮.

Harmonic

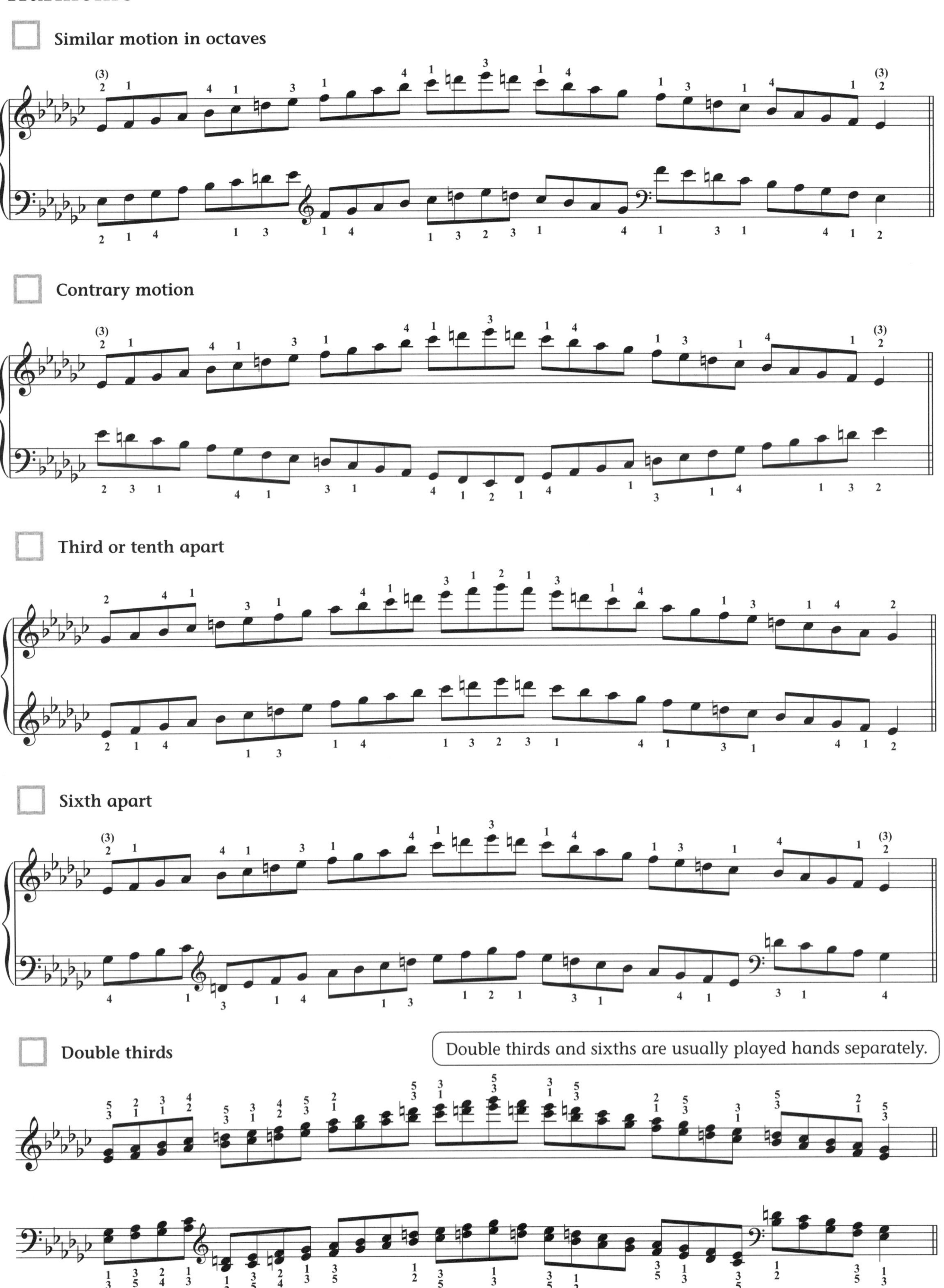

Melodic

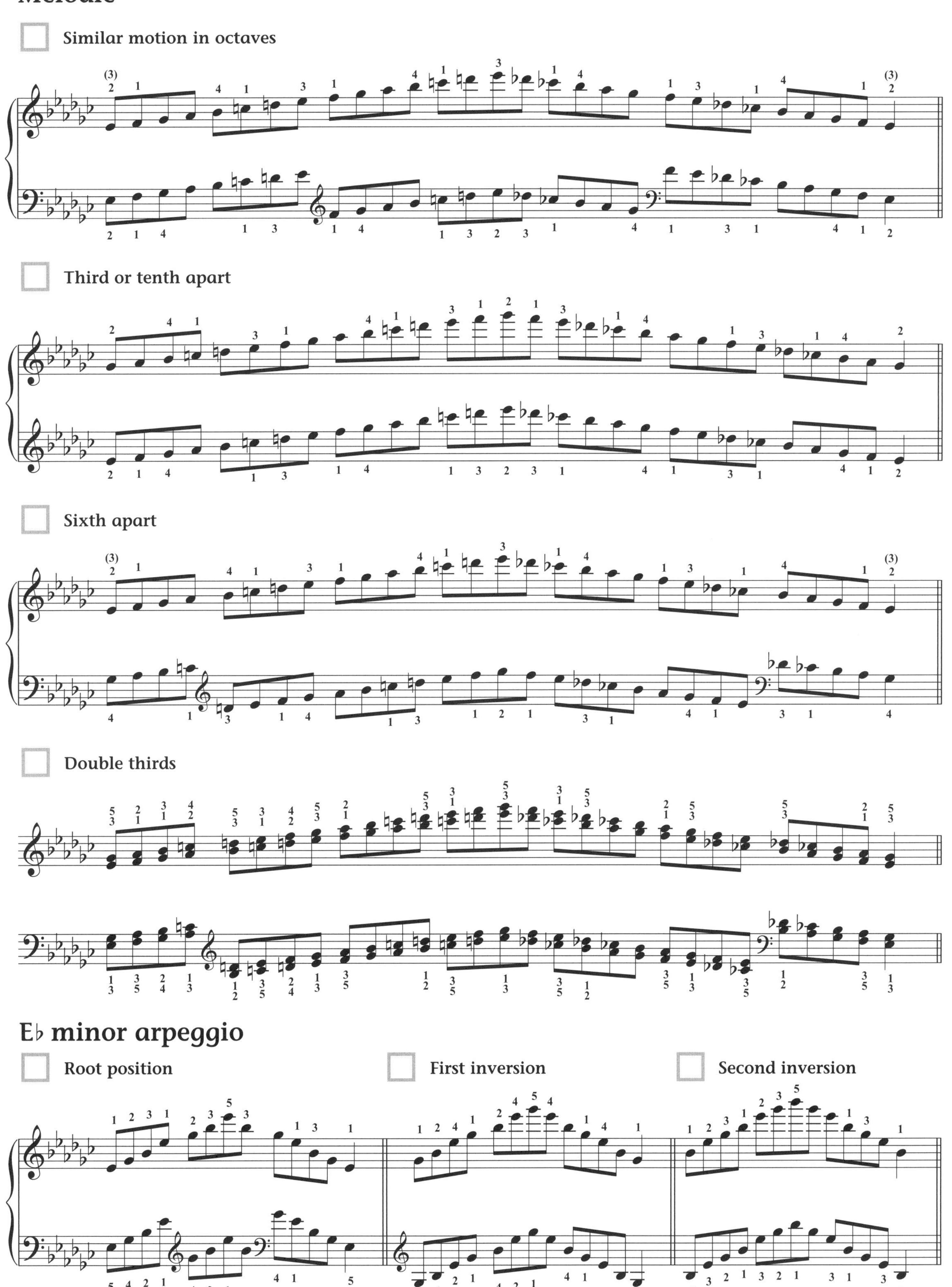

Similar motion in octaves
Third or tenth apart
Sixth apart
Double thirds
E♭ minor arpeggio
Root position
First inversion
Second inversion

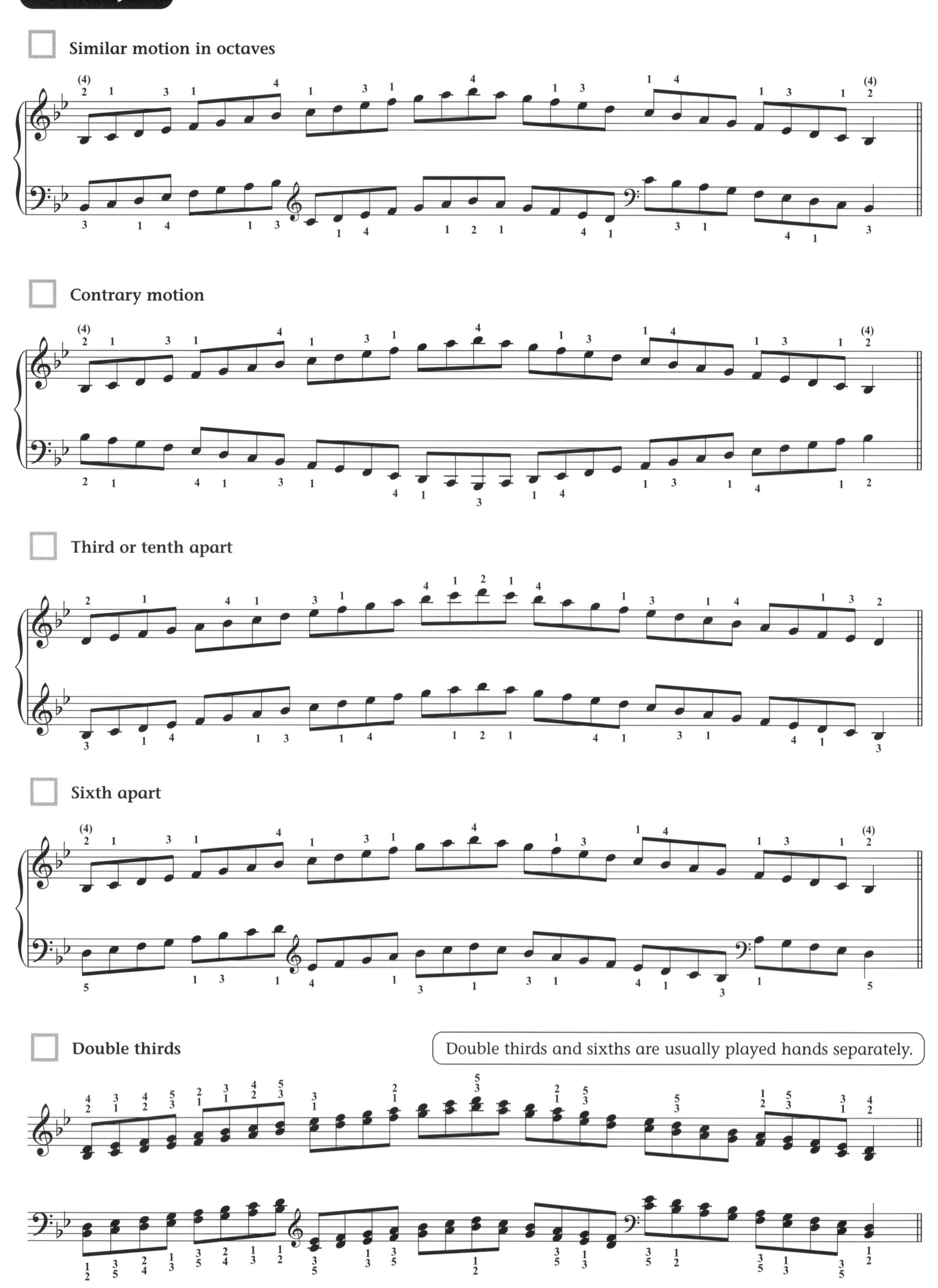
B♭ major
The relative minor of B♭ major is G minor.
Similar motion in octaves
Contrary motion
Third or tenth apart
Sixth apart
Double thirds
Double thirds and sixths are usually played hands separately.

B♭ major arpeggio

Root position

First inversion

Second inversion

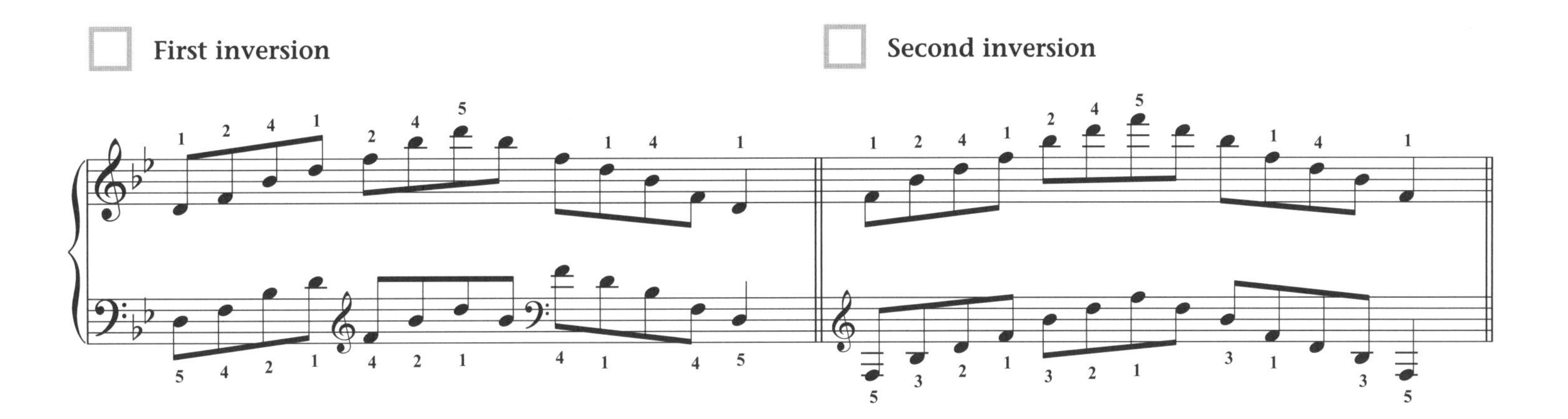

Dominant and diminished sevenths

Dominant seventh in B♭

Diminished seventh on B♭

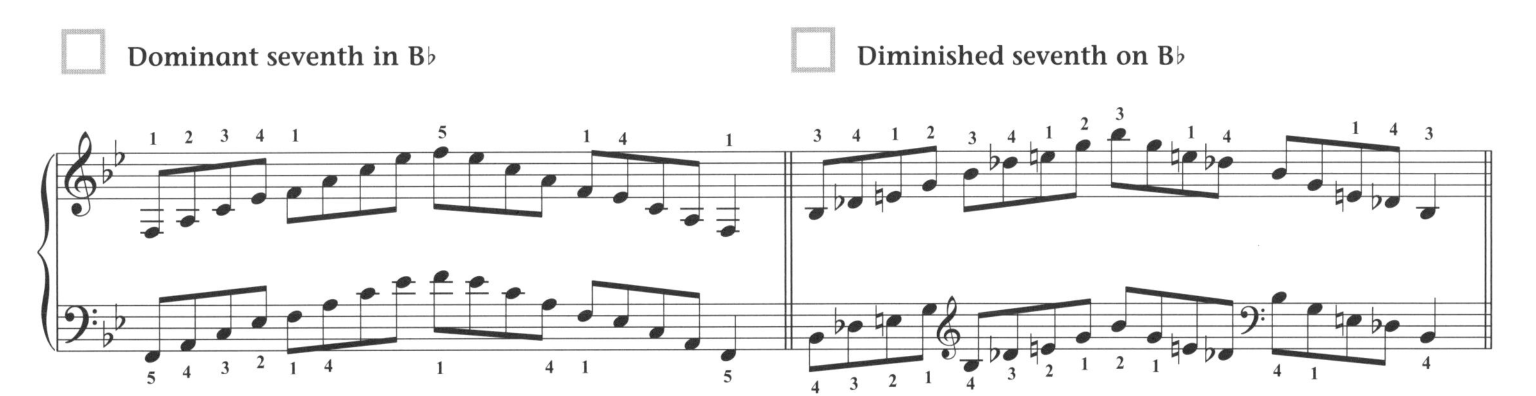

Hints and tips

- Scales in double thirds can be fingered in many ways; the system adopted here is the 'two group' fingering. Each octave is divided into a 3-note and 4-note group, the longer group using the gliding thumb.
- As well as practising using different variations of touch, tone, rhythm and range, you could try playing scales and arpeggios in keys related to B♭ major: the relative minor (G minor), the dominant (F major), the subdominant (E♭ major) and the tonic minor (B♭ minor).
- Using the 3rd finger where 4th is stipulated in arpeggios is accepted by some pianists, but it is better to train the weaker 4th finger from the earliest lessons to encourage proper, systematic hand shape development.

B♭ minor

The relative major of B♭ minor is D♭ major.
Watch out for the raised seventh in B♭ minor: A♮.

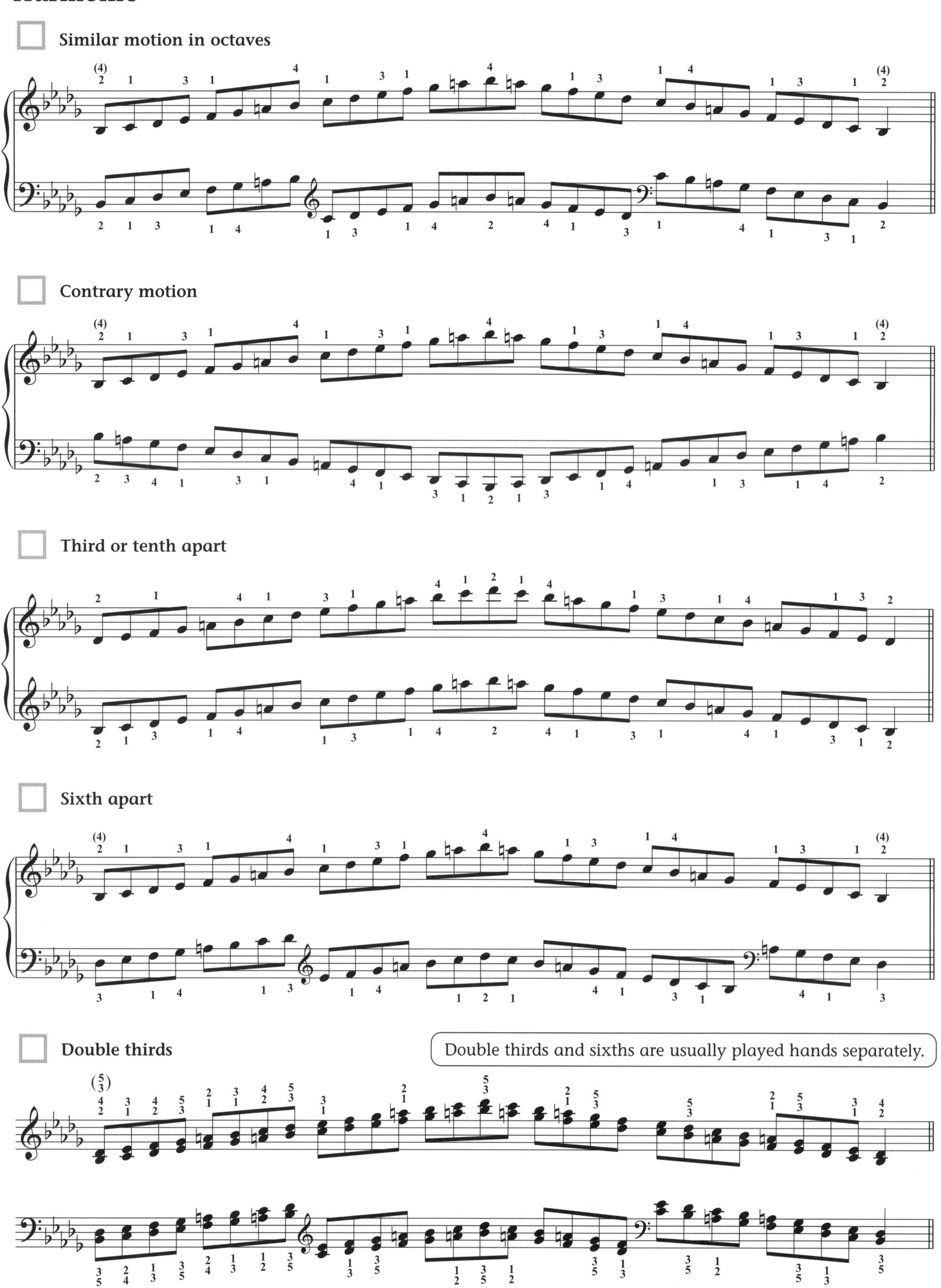

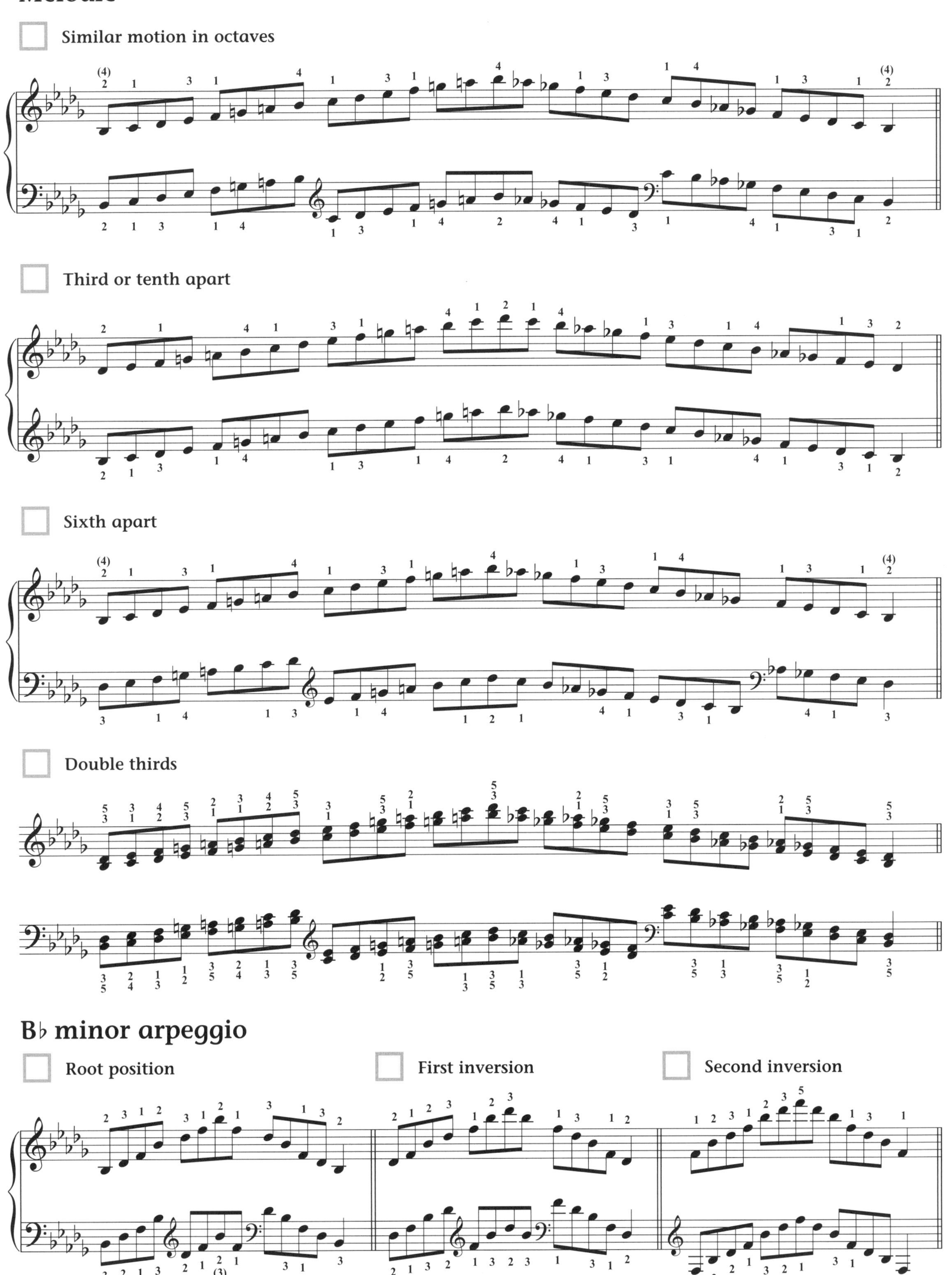
Melodic
Similar motion in octaves
Third or tenth apart
Sixth apart
Double thirds
B♭ minor arpeggio
Root position
First inversion
Second inversion

F major

The relative minor of F major is D minor.

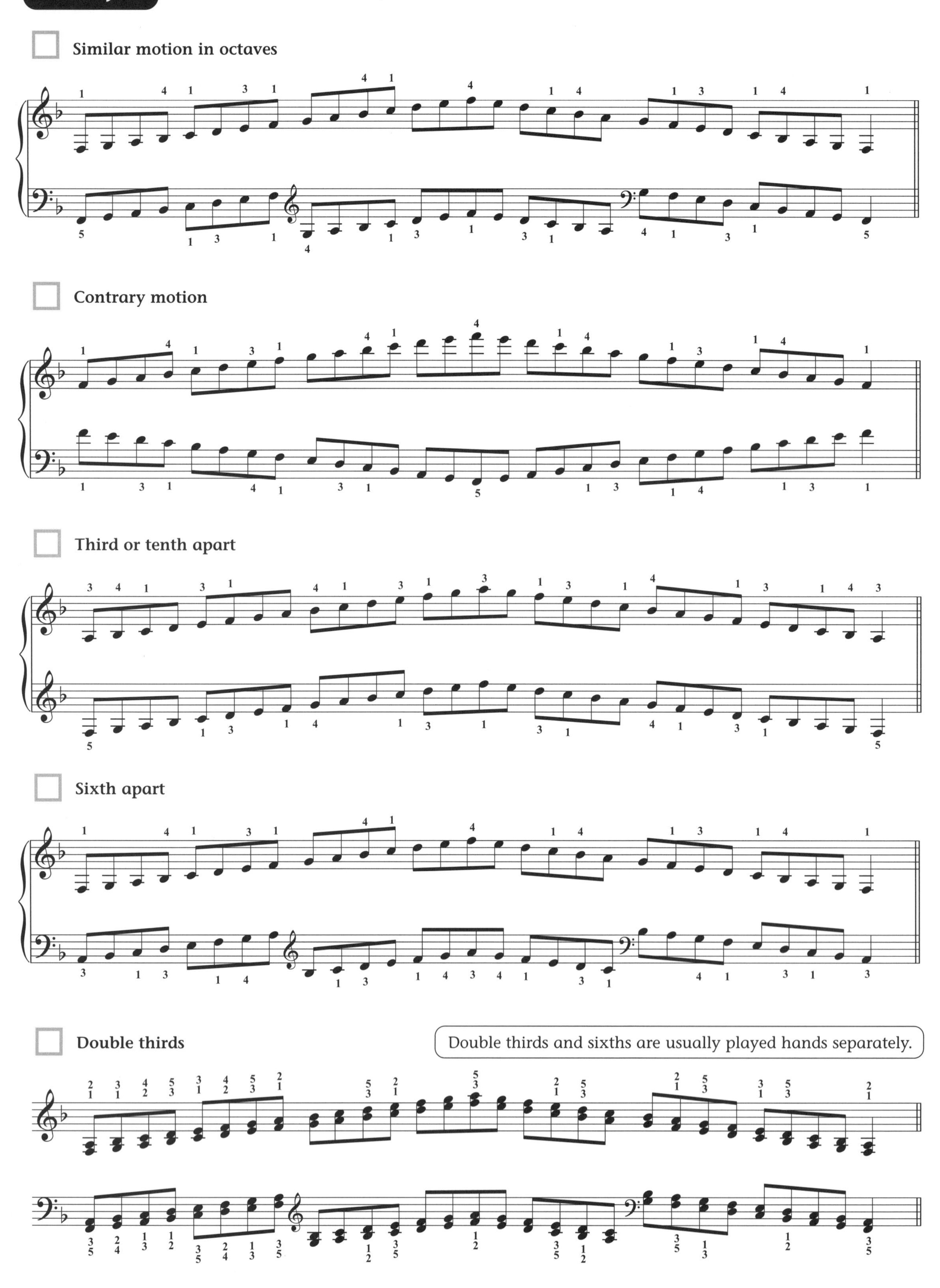

F major arpeggio

☐ Root position

☐ First inversion

☐ Second inversion

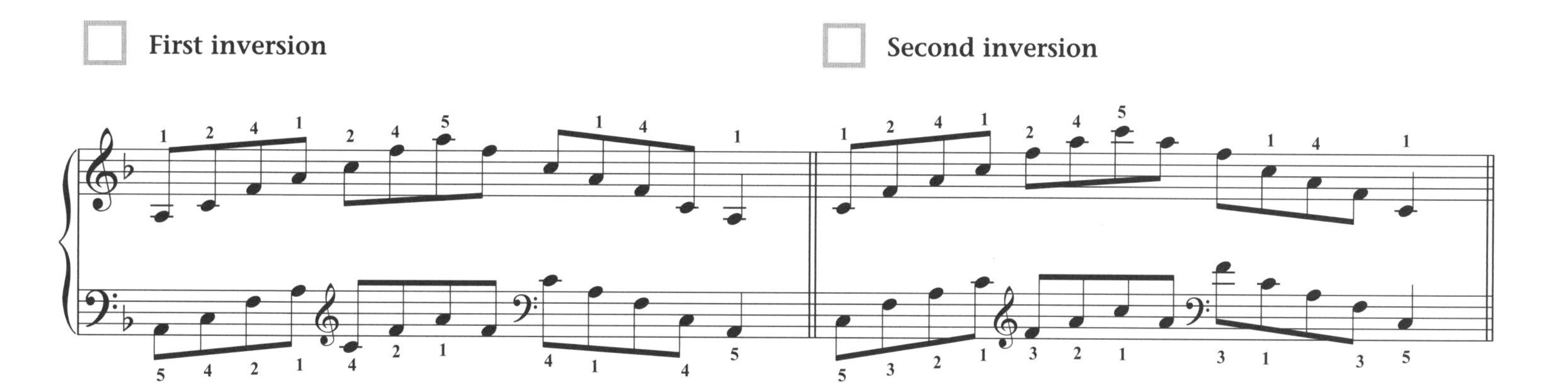

Dominant and diminished sevenths

☐ Dominant seventh in F

☐ Diminished seventh on F

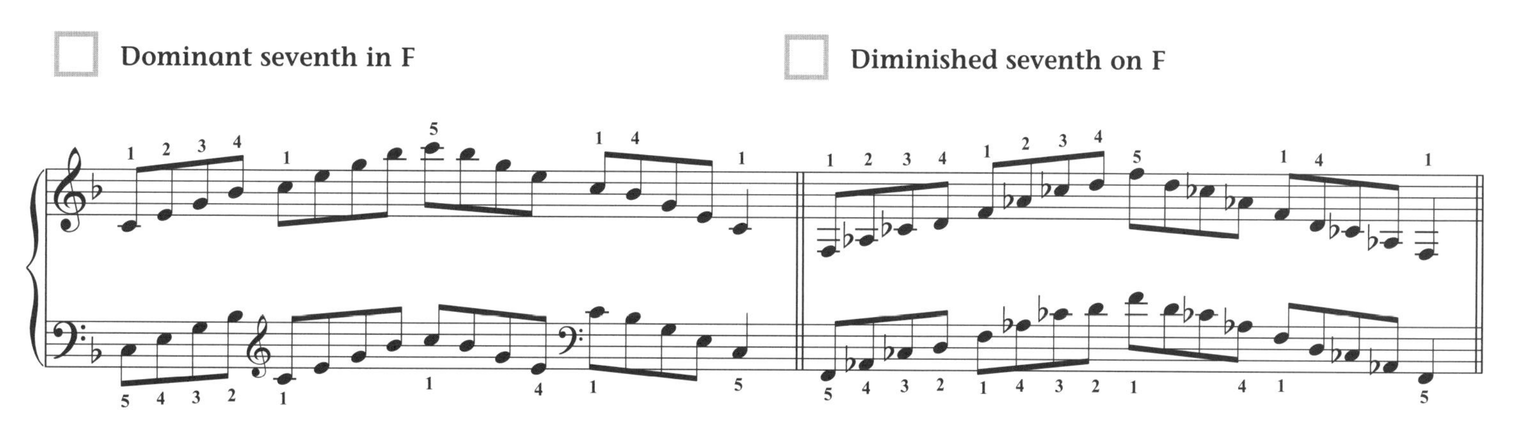

Hints and tips

- Scales in double thirds can be fingered in many ways; the system adopted here is the 'two group' fingering. Each octave is divided into a 3-note and 4-note group, the longer group using the gliding thumb.
- As well as practising using different variations of touch, tone, rhythm and range, you could try playing scales and arpeggios in keys related to F major: the relative minor (D minor), the dominant (C major), the subdominant (B♭ major) and the tonic minor (F minor).
- Using the 3rd finger where 4th is stipulated in arpeggios is accepted by some pianists, but it is better to train the weaker 4th finger from the earliest lessons to encourage proper, systematic hand shape development.

F minor

The relative major of F minor is A♭ major.
Watch out for the raised seventh in F minor: E♮.

Harmonic

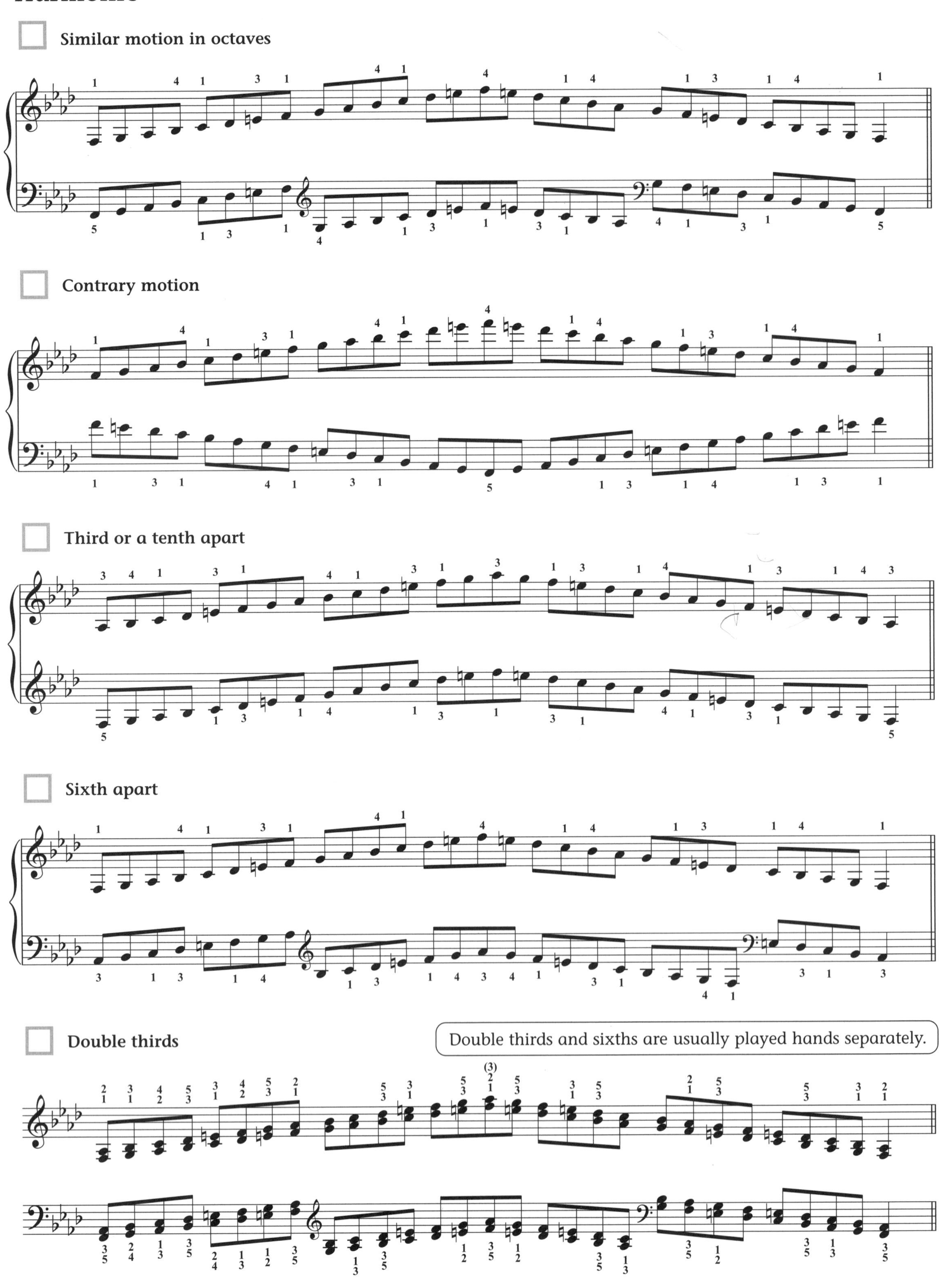

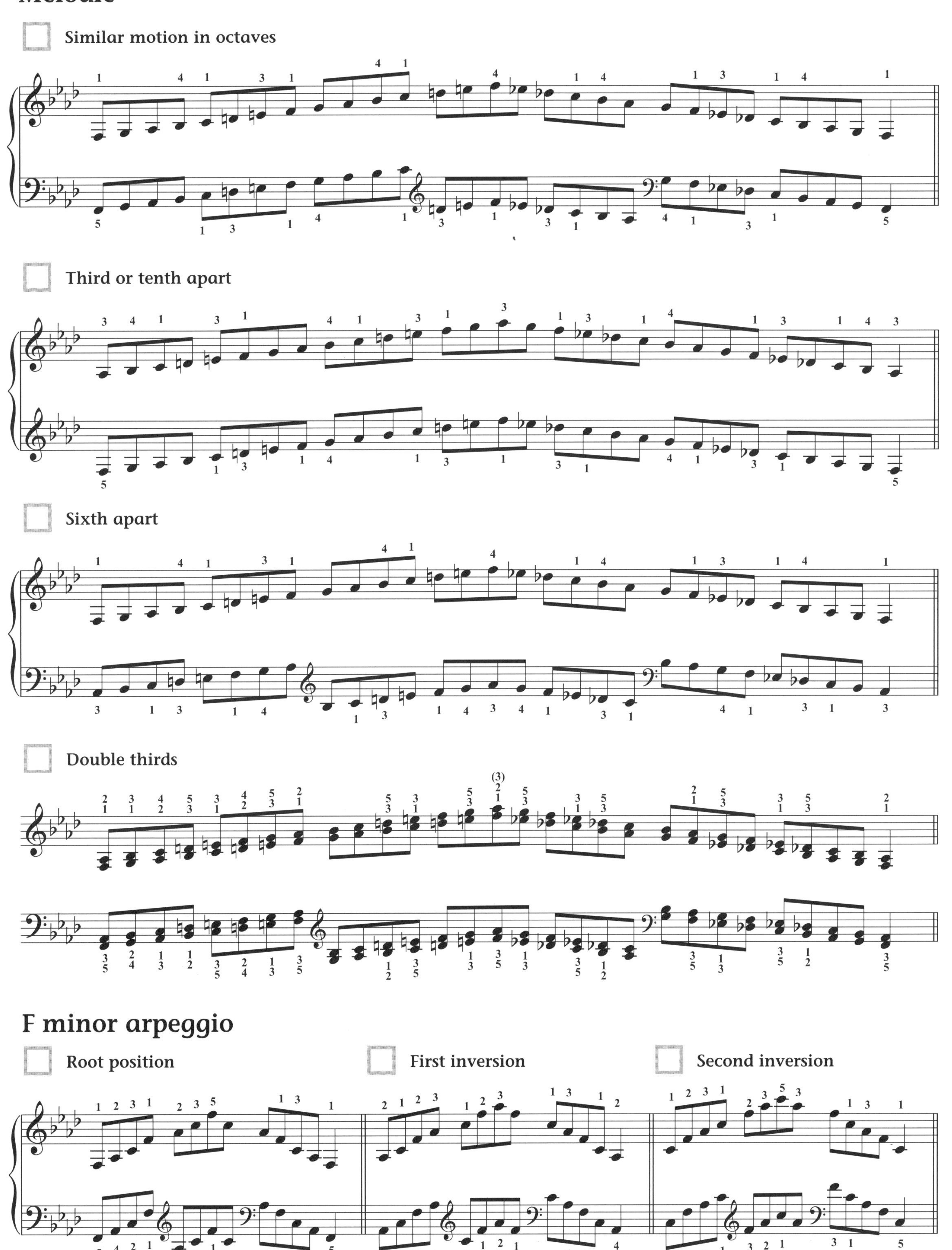
Melodic
Similar motion in octaves
Third or tenth apart
Sixth apart
Double thirds
F minor arpeggio
Root position
First inversion
Second inversion

Chromatics

A chromatic scale is made up of twelve semitones and always follows the same pattern of fingering.

Similar motion in octaves

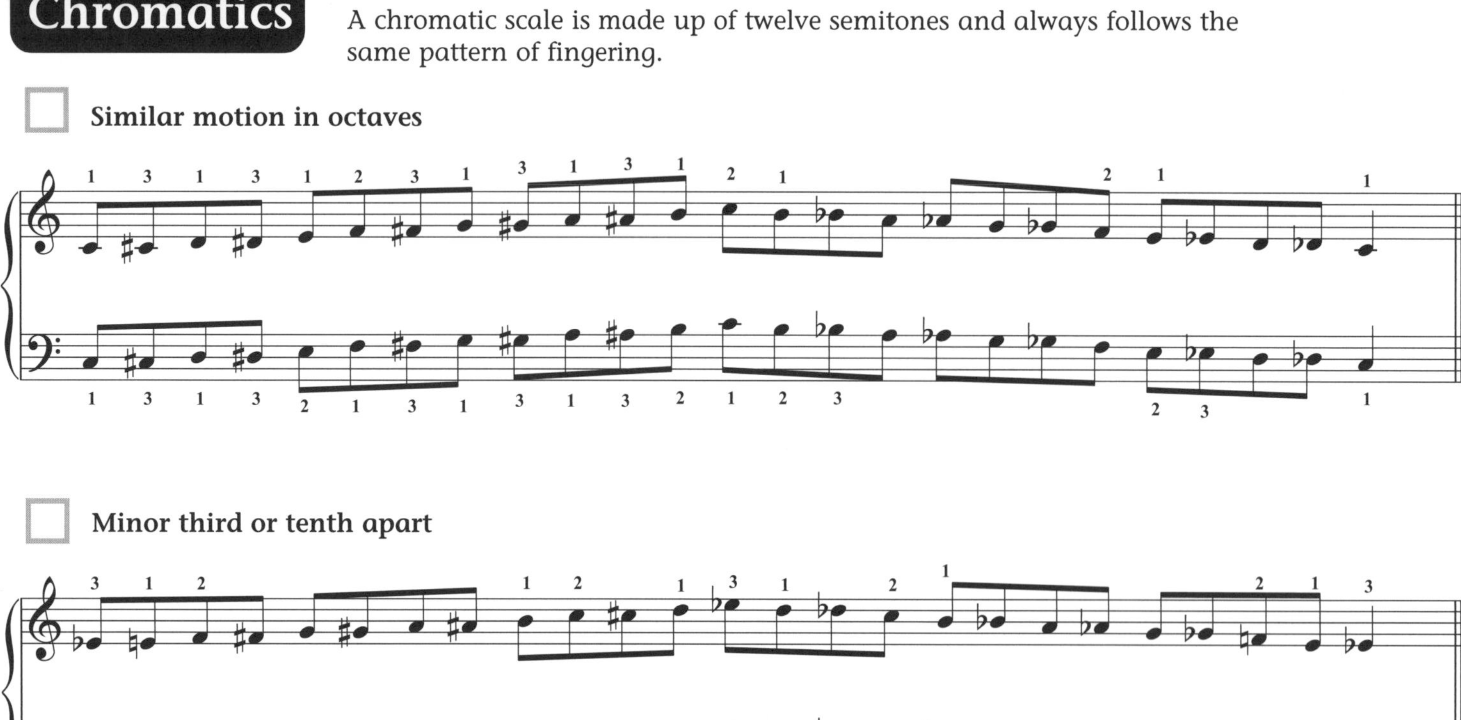

Minor third or tenth apart

Major sixth apart

Contrary motion

Double thirds

Double thirds and sixths are usually played hands separately.

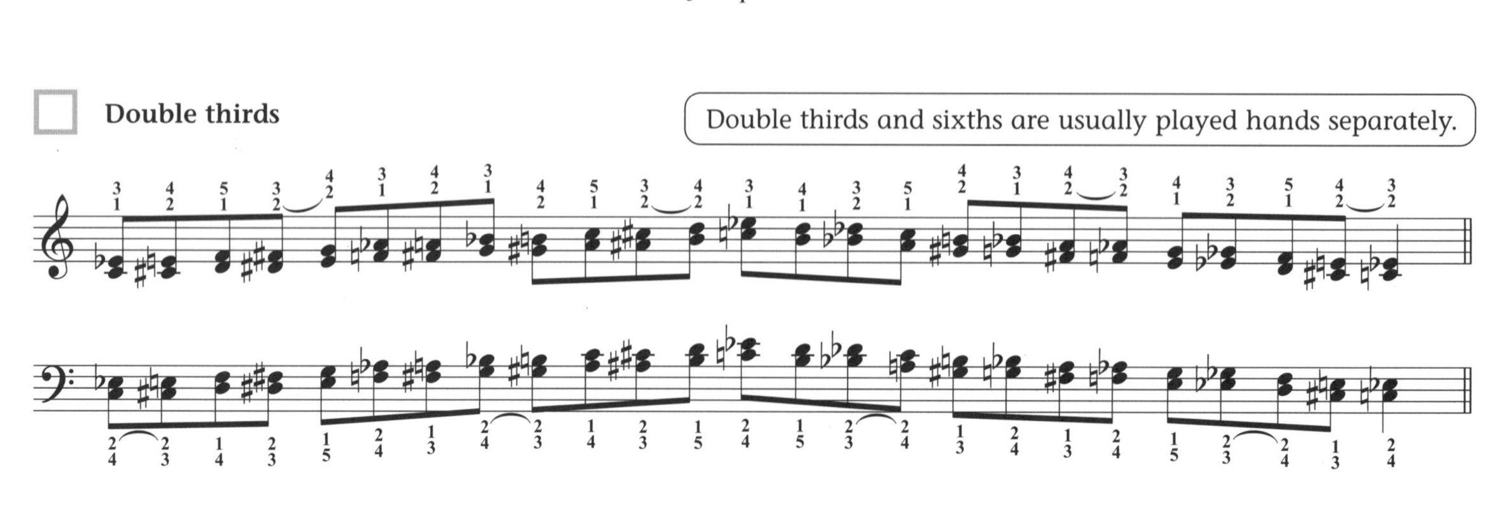

Whole-tone scales

A whole-tone scale is formed by taking every other note of the chromatic scale. Only two whole-tone scales are therefore possible.

Starting on C

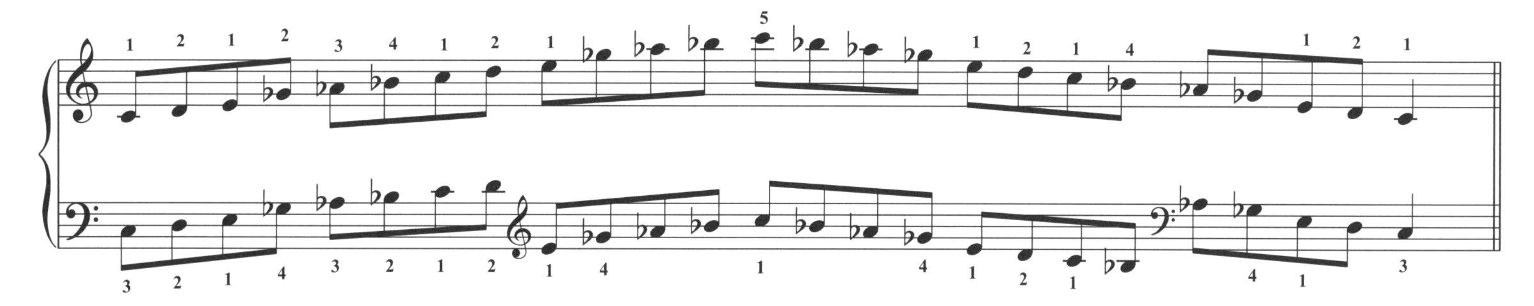

Contrary motion

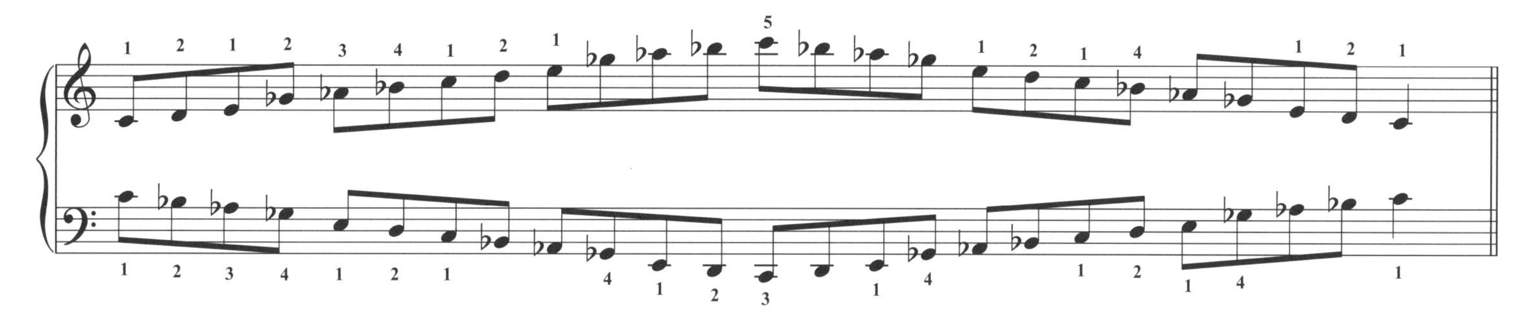

Starting on B

Contrary motion

Double octaves

Only three examples are given here as all double octave scales follow the same pattern: 4th finger on black notes which follow a white note (not on black notes following black notes). The fingering pattern can therefore change descending. The result can then be *quasi-legato* or *bravura detaché*, as required.

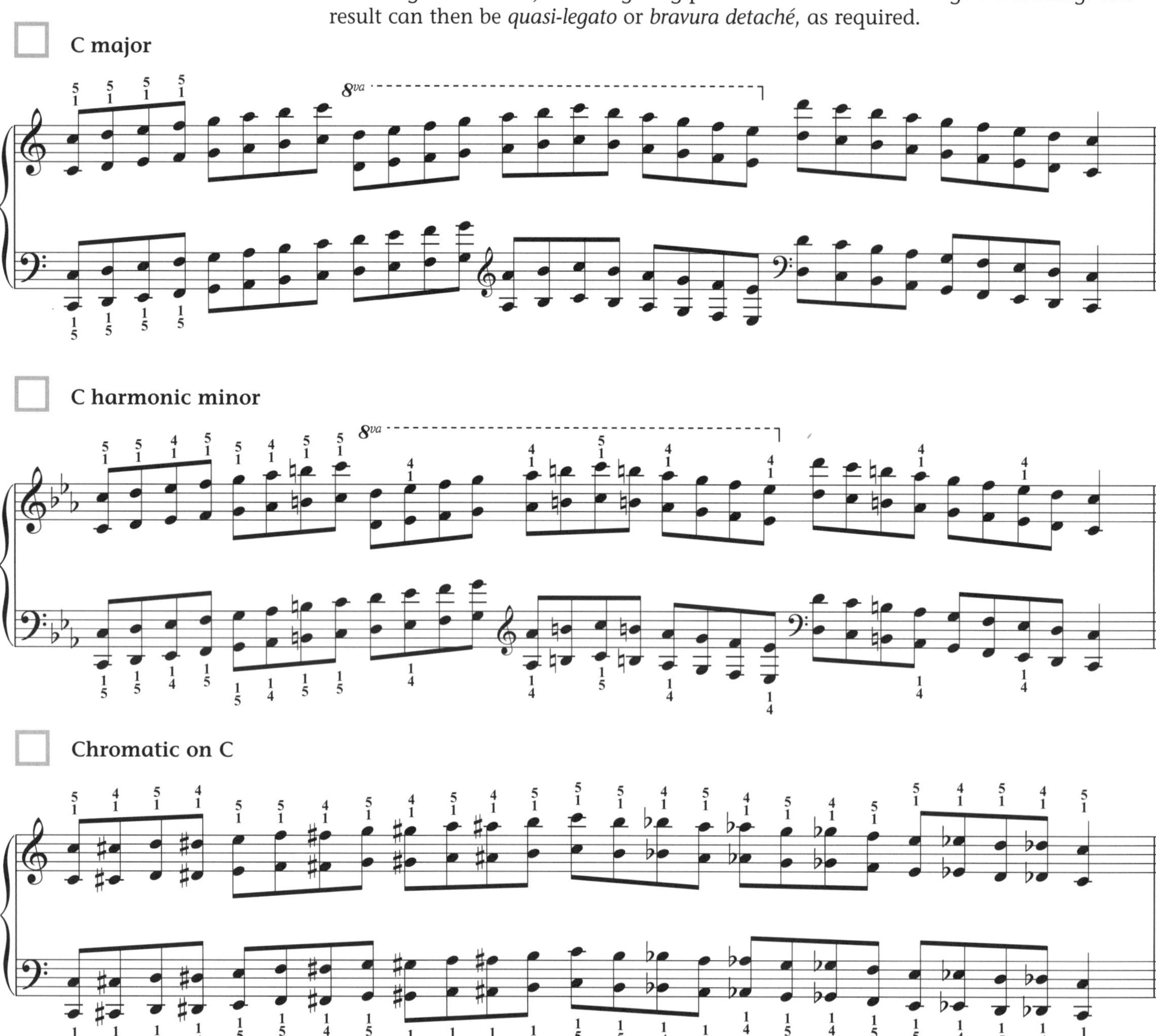

As an alternative, octave scales may be played 1-5 throughout. This is especially useful for hands too small to play 1-4.

Double sixths

Usually required *staccato*, hands separately, using the same finger pattern for all scales.

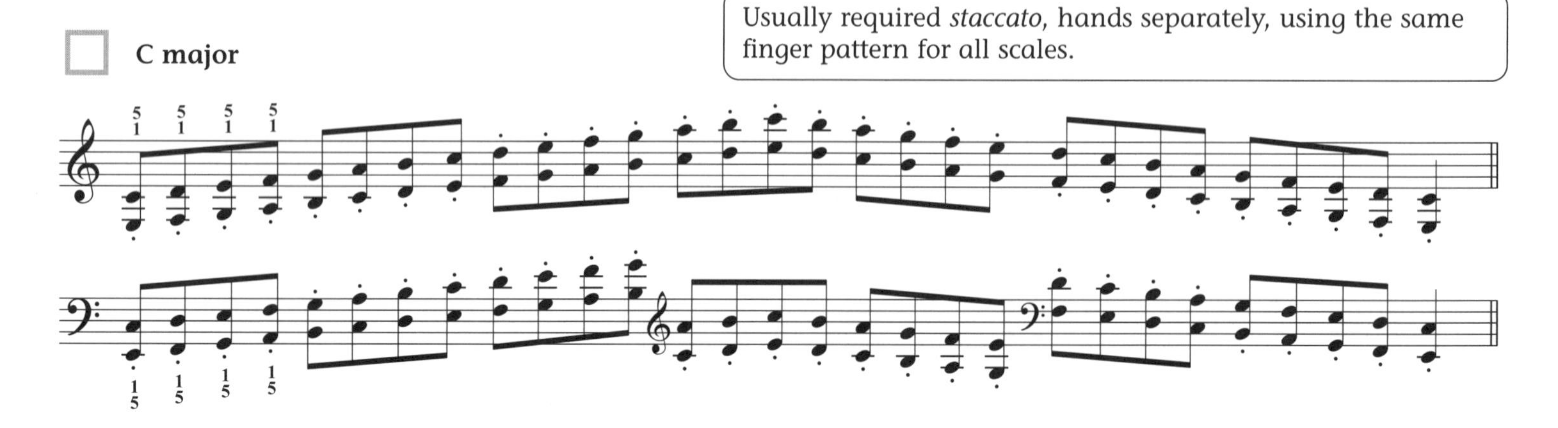

A pentatonic scale is made up of five notes. The following pattern is known as the 'major' pentatonic and uses notes 1, 2, 3, 5 and 6 of the major scale.

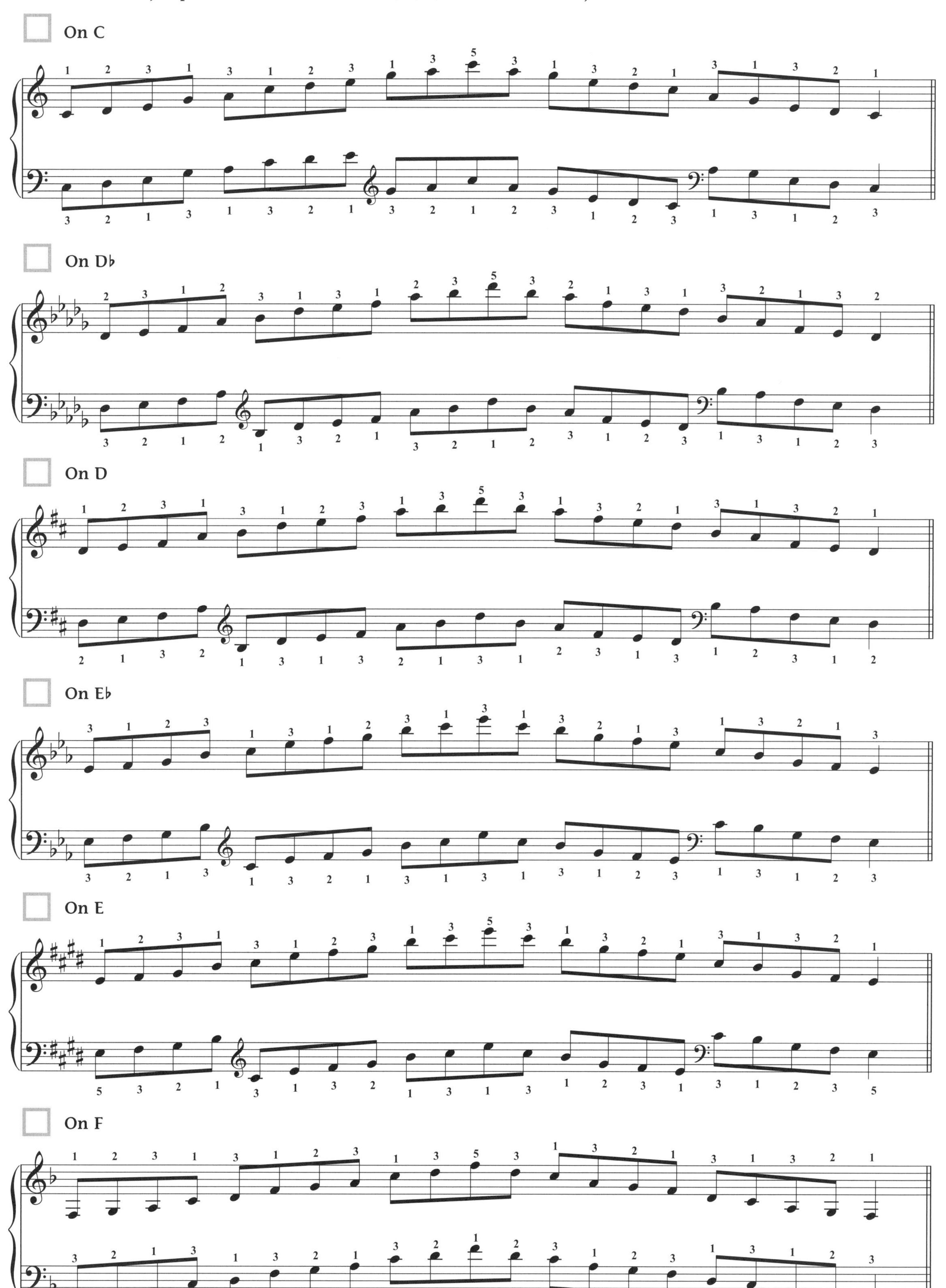

Pentatonic scales
On F♯
On G
On A♭
On A
On B♭
On B
56

Blues scales

These blues scales can be used as a resource for improvisation. The fingering is designed to give fluency over two octaves; it can be varied within shorter melodic cells.

☐ **On C**

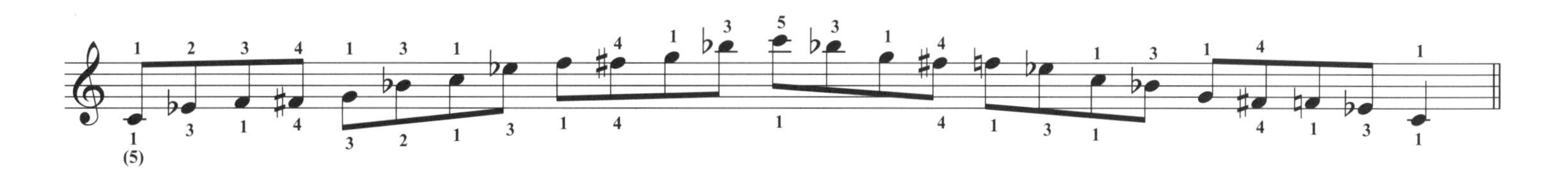

☐ **On D♭**

☐ **On D**

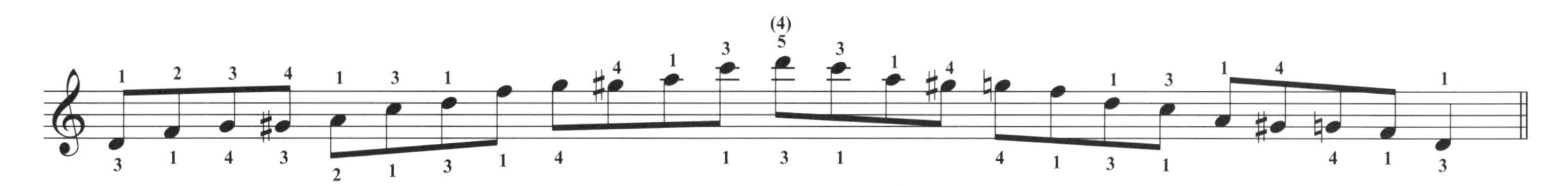

☐ **On E♭**

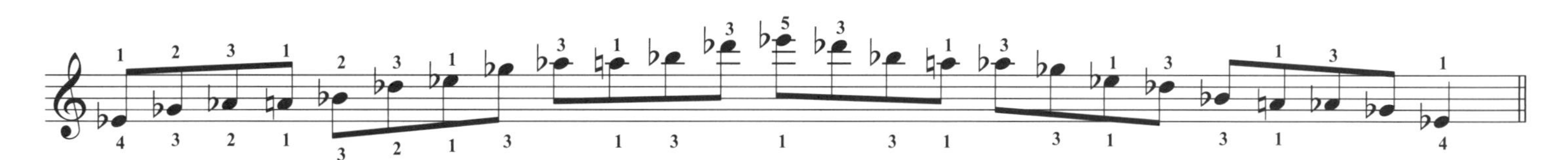

☐ **On E**

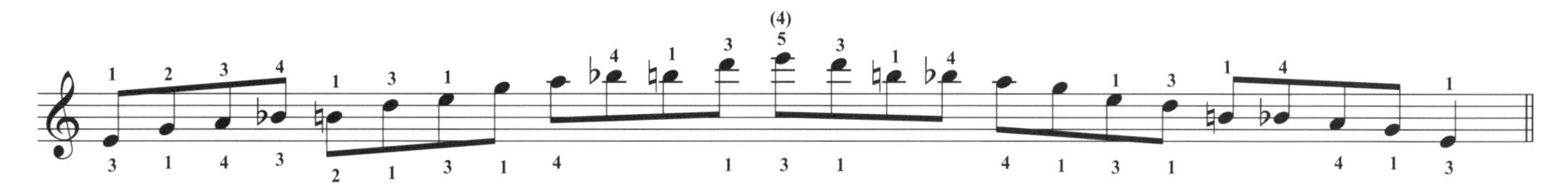

☐ **On F**

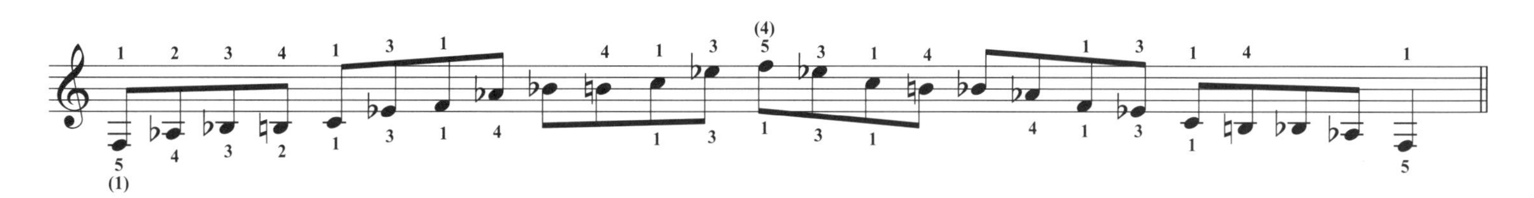

Blues scales

 On F♯

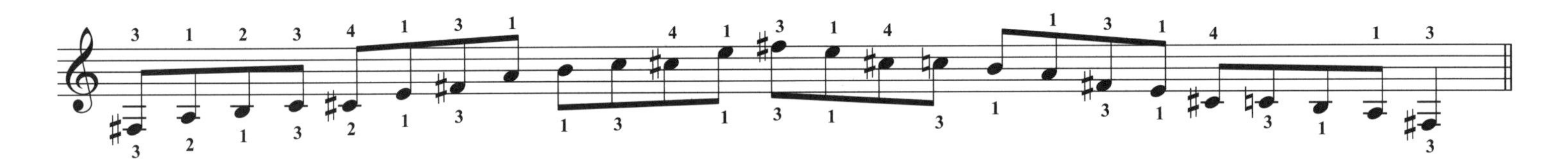

On G

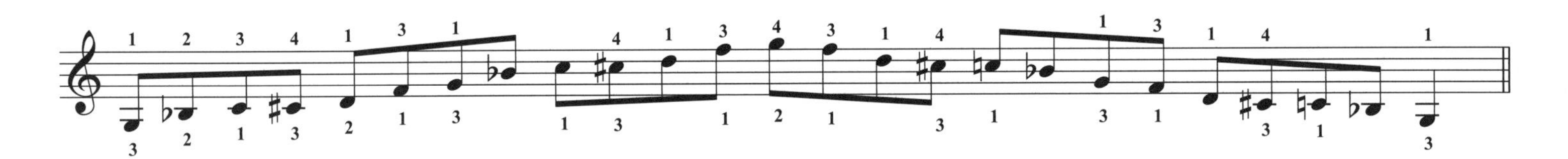

On G♯

On A

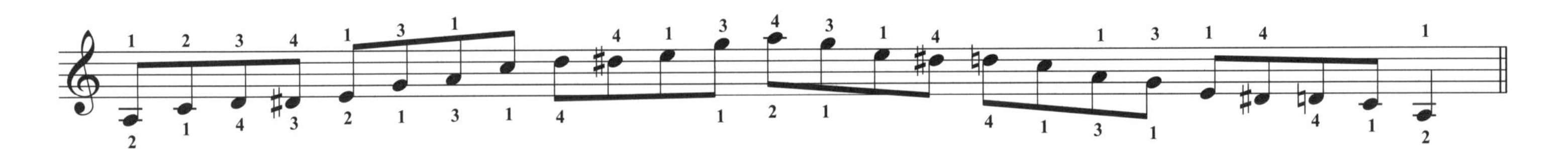

On B♭

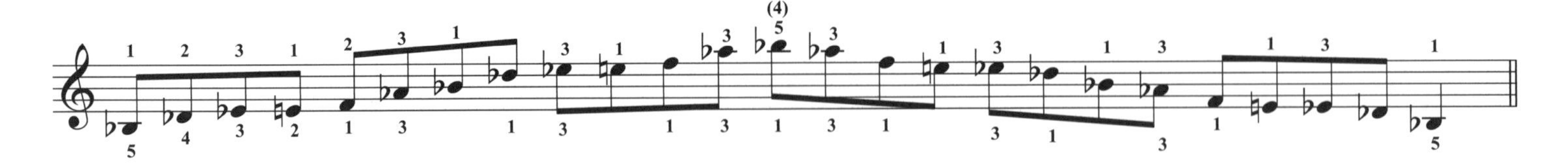

On B

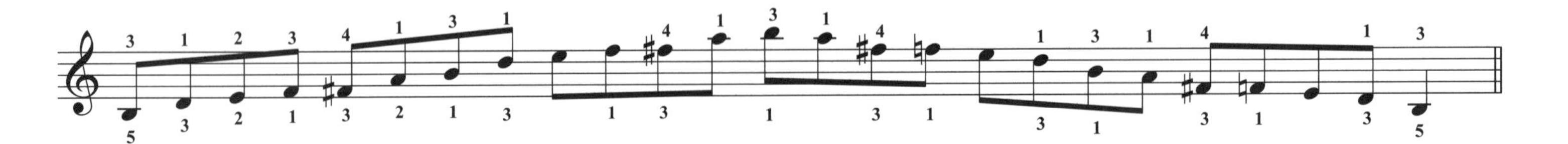

Learning scales and arpeggios

Scales

All major and minor scales have the same fingering but with different starting points, depending on the distribution of black keys. A scale consists of alternating three-finger and four-finger groups, the thumb passing under the third or the fourth finger and the third or fourth finger passing over the thumb. That's the whole picture – easily learnt, readily repeated and extended – and not complicated!

It follows that it is best to think of each scale as a repeating group pattern, as short series of notes following on logically and repetitively, rather than a selection of random notes. In this way, the thumb-passing and finger-over-the-thumb movements become more meaningful, fluent, forward-looking and more musically generated.

Arpeggios

Arpeggios, too, should be understood as musical building blocks. Their point is to develop good hand shape, extension, fluency about the keyboard and strong chord playing, as well as to instil and train the essential 'feel' that each key has under the hand.

Learning scales

Here's one way (and there are many more) of learning scales easily and confidently.

- Choose any scale and locate the two thumb notes in each octave.
- Play the first thumb note and, with a perfect *legato*, add the two- or three-note group (2, 3 or 2, 3, 4) as a chord above it (RH) or below it (LH).
- Hold the chord, to learn its distinctive shape combining black and white keys, and release the thumb.
- With a well-poised, relaxed and curved (bridged) hand pass the thumb through and under the held chord to the next thumb note. As you play this, release the chord just played and reposition the hand quickly for the next group, again playing it as a chord.

These chords may sound dissonant, but the hand will learn the feel of the key, the spacing and the group-fingering! Familiarity leads to fluency, strength and confidence.

Learning arpeggios

This 'grouping system' does not work for arpeggios with young players because the spacing is too big. However, the sooner the player realises that the fingering of all arpeggios and inversions depends on the shape of the whole octave chord the better the result and effect. Just compare the chords of C minor with D major (left hand), or D flat major with E flat minor (right hand) to appreciate immediately when to use 3 and when to use 4.

- Thumb passing is more problematic in arpeggios than in scales but it should initially be done as *legato* as possible. (More advanced players will 'adapt' the *legato* as required by context and speed.)
- Ideally, the hand should be allowed to 'close in' naturally as it moves through the arpeggio, and not be left stranded and stretched out.
- A good practice trick is to play the thumb note and add first one note above and one below (with the correct fingers of course), then two notes, swinging round and over the thumb as *legato* and relaxed as possible but with a strong tone. Avoid the temptation to let the elbows kick out!
- Allow no lazy, unproductive use of the third where the fourth is better! We need all the fingers to do equal service and any neglect of four will only have to be rectified later.
- Dominant and diminished sevenths should only be tackled by more advanced players whose hands can cope with their demands. But as with ordinary arpeggios, allowing the hand to relax and close naturally after extension is essential if pains and stress are to be avoided.

Practising scales and arpeggios

Using variations to practise

Once fingering and notes are fluent, with a good, even, *legato cantabile* tone, any scale or arpeggio can be usefully subjected to variations of touch, tone, rhythm and range. There is no need to be bored by scale practice! Try experimenting with the following areas:

- dynamic colour
- *crescendo/diminuendo*
- differing degrees of *staccato*
- dotted rhythms
- irregular rhythmic groups (e.g. triplets, quintuplets)
- uneven repeated rhythms
- combining duplets in one hand with triplets in the other
- alternating contrary motion with similar motion
- starting very slow and accelerating
- beginning a scale on the dominant

Any of these variations will add interest and the range is limitless. See page 63 for some specific ideas to get you started.

How to group scales and arpeggios for practice

Apart from the keys required for any particular grade examination, it is always more interesting musically to understand scales and arpeggios in related key-groups, so that the 12 majors and 24 minors don't simply loom threateningly, just out of reach. Here are some ideas of different ways you could group keys for practice:

- According to key signature: for example linking keys with three sharps with those with three flats.
- Connecting relative major/minor (so with the same key signature).
- Moving through the cycle of fifths, up through the sharps or down through the flats (see page 64).
- By linking keys with the same arpeggio pattern: D, E and A majors are all the same; C, F and G minors are another group; C, F and G majors with D, E and A minors are another group, while A flat, D flat and E flat majors are yet another group pattern.
- By the keys of the pieces currently being studied – an absolute must!

Any of the above systems encourages awareness of key-relationship and difference in a musically positive way. Don't just work at the minimum requirements for a grade examination. Every key has a near relative worth a visit. Try the dominant key (i.e. one more sharp or one less flat), subdominant (i.e. one less sharp or one more flat), relative major/minor, or tonic major/minor (i.e. the opposite mode but with the same letter name). All of these have the added advantage of familiarising the player with some of music's technical terms and tonal grounding.

Incorporating scales and arpeggios in your practice time

It is a good habit to begin each practice session with a warm-up involving some slow scales and arpeggios to stretch the hands and fingers and get the ears alert to tonal evenness. Then go further, taking one key and working it thoroughly through, varying dynamics, speeds and touches. Don't let your mind wander off. Tell yourself that the music you will soon be playing will gain from these brief minutes of self discipline and that you will be in better shape for it. Never forget that music, for most of the last 400 years, has been key-centred and that the keyboard, by its nature, feels different in each key.

Scales and arpeggios in examinations

Scales and arpeggios do not exist in an examination context only! Of course they figure in that system and probably always will, but not because the exam boards are mean-spirited. The percentage of marks allocated to them reflects their relative importance alongside pieces, sight-reading, aural tests and so on. Reasons for examining scales and arpeggios include:

- To encourage a properly organised and structured development of technical and musical understanding, encompassing speed, tone, fluency, evenness and so on.
- To extend the player's familiarity with the keyboard beyond the middle registers inhabited by so much of the more elementary repertoire.
- To prepare a player for the 'nuts and bolts' of all music.
- To ensure good habits right from the start – and habits are only gained through repetition.

Within an examination context, scales and arpeggios are a useful gauge of the level of expertise achieved but are not to be feared, nor should they assume an overbearing status. The question of how fast they should be played in the exam is open to debate: aim for fluency and consistent evenness of tone. Better to play fluent but slowish scales and arpeggios than quick but faulty ones.

Health and safety issues

Any pain or discomfort that arises during practice can be a result of poor posture, muscle tiredness and associated mis-use of muscles or insufficient warming up. It is important to recognise early on the difference between mere fatigue, easily remedied with a break, and more serious potential damage. The following points are important to bear in mind:

- Any pain or discomfort must be addressed immediately and, if necessary, advice sought from a professional.
- Never lift the shoulders: their vital role is in tone production and they need to be free.
- Forearms should be on a level with the keyboard or slightly downhill to the keyboard – a matter of personal comfort and efficient use of arm weight.
- There should be at all times a feeling of relaxation in the arms, heaviness in the forearms and flexibility in the wrists.
- Any strong muscle movement should be balanced immediately by a release of tension: action and reaction.
- *Legato* playing is less strenuous than *staccato* but must not be confused with dull-toned, colourless playing.
- As you move to the extremities of the keyboard, don't adopt an awkward posture. It is fine to lean over (without losing your balance) and to move to the right or left on the stool.

Short, productive and frequent practice sessions are infinitely better than last-minute marathon sessions with the danger of muscle pain and exhaustion. Older players will usually have more stamina, but all players should take a short break if necessary before continuing an enjoyable practice session.

A note about *staccato*

Playing staccato is often a cause of tension leading to muscle strain, aches and pains.

- *Staccato from the finger only* (articulating only from the knuckle) is good for light, soft, fast playing; but don't forget to relax the 'unused' wrist and forearm.
- *Staccato from the hand* (articulating from the wrist) requires the hand to be well curved and relaxed, not flapping flatly, so that the fingers are braced and the fingertips are available to strike the keys. Generally it works at slower speeds than finger staccato.
- *Staccato from the forearm* (articulating from the elbow) is a more advanced technique, an

Practice planner

This page may be photocopied.

Scale/arpeggio	Practice programme	Comments

Practice variations

Play with hands separately

Crescendo up, *diminuendo* down

Play with a dotted rhythm:

Play *mezzo forte*

Play with this articulation:

Play with a swung rhythm:

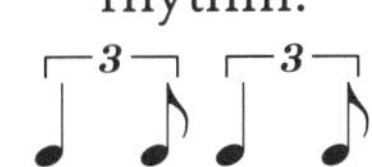

Play *piano*

Play very slowly

Play with a dotted rhythm:

Begin on the dominant note

Play with this articulation:

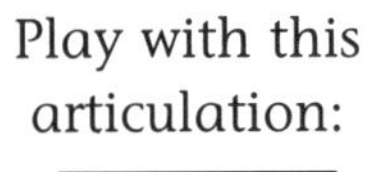

Play *forte*

Play with this articulation:

Play *forte staccato*

Play two octaves apart

Play in a triplet rhythm (3 octaves):

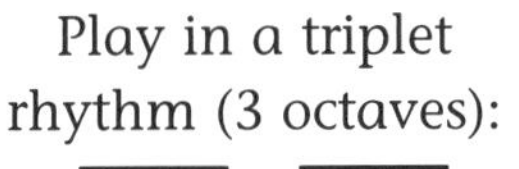

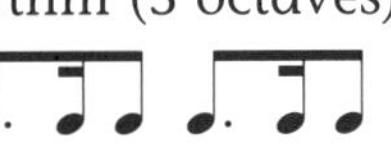

Play in broken 3rds:

Play *leggiero*, lightly staccato

Play with this rhythm:

Play with this articulation:

Play with this articulation:

Play in contrary motion

Start at the top, descend then ascend

Play with this rhythm:

Circle of fifths

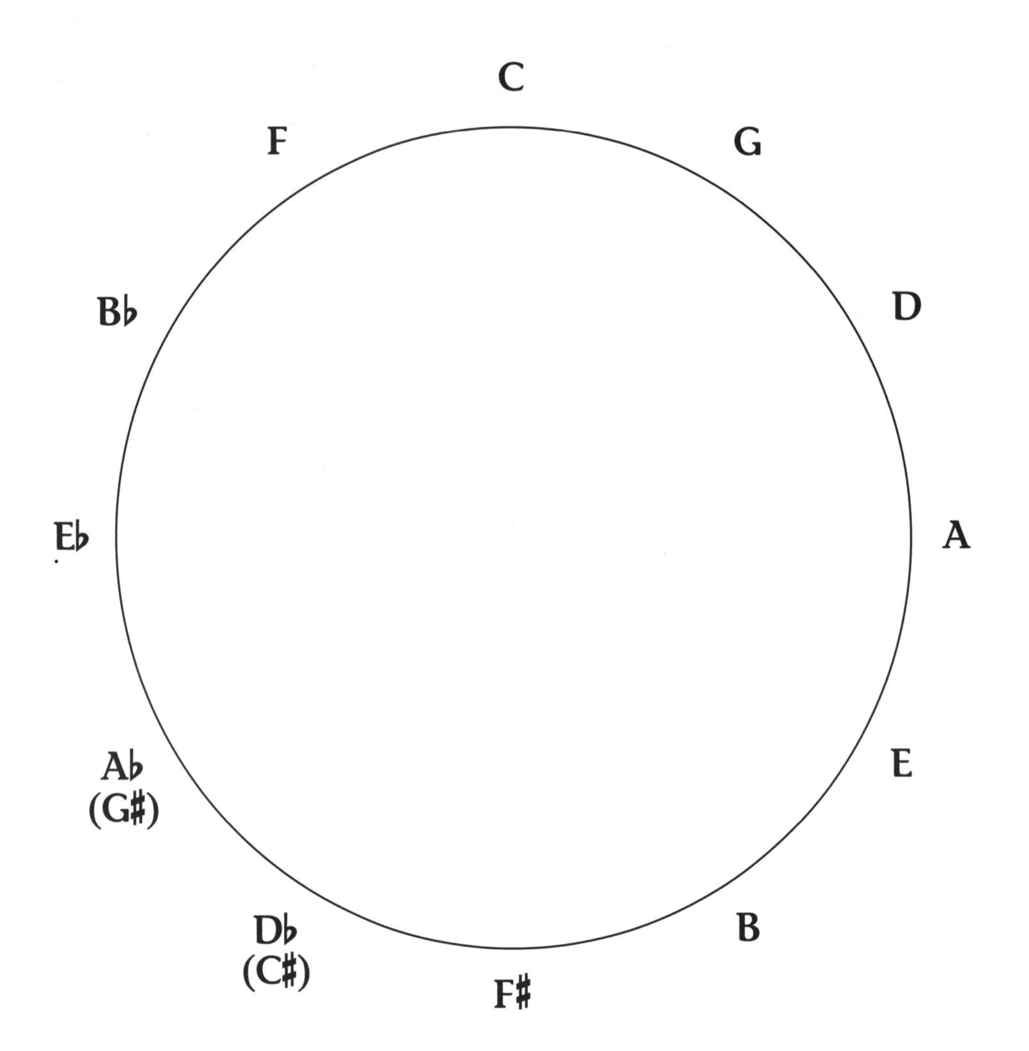